PRENTICE HALL
WRITING & GRAMMAR

Formal Assessment
Blackline Masters

Grade Twelve

PEARSON

Prentice
Hall

Boston, Massachusetts,
Upper Saddle River, New Jersey

Pearson Prentice Hall™ is a trademark of Pearson Education, Inc.
Pearson® is a registered trademark of Pearson plc.
Prentice Hall® is a registered trademark of Pearson Education, Inc.

ISBN 0-13-361522-7

1 2 3 4 5 6 7 8 9 10   10 09 08 07

Contents

About the Tests

This Formal Assessment booklet contains one test for each chapter in the *Writing and Grammar* student textbook. To provide you with the greatest flexibility, the tests utilize a number of different formats and may be administered in one or more class periods, depending on your classroom needs and your students' abilities. The complete Formal Assessment program is also available on a Computer Test Bank CD-ROM.

Tests for Part 1: Writing

■ With the exception of the tests on the Documented Essay, Research, and Workplace Writing chapters, the tests on the modes of writing ask students to write a brief paper, applying the skills taught in the chapter. The questions on the tests are designed to lead the students through the writing process. Depending on your students' abilities, you may assign the tests to be done in one class period or as an extended assignment. Three tests (1—easy, 2—average, and 3—challenging) are provided for each mode of writing, the difference in the levels of difficulty being the complexity of the assignment and of some of the tasks students are asked to complete.

■ Using multiple-choice and short-answer formats, the tests for Chapters 1, 2, and 3 and for the Documented Essay, Research, and Workplace Writing chapters ask students to recognize, respond to, and evaluate the material taught in the chapters.

Tests for Part 2: Grammar, Usage, and Mechanics

■ Part 2 contains extensive objective tests on all the grammar, usage, and mechanics topics taught in the student textbook. Each test ends with a question bank in one of several standardized-test formats. In the answer key at the back of the booklet, you will find a level designation—easy, average, or challenging—for each question. These designations, together with the ample number of questions provided, give you the flexibility of customizing the tests for individual students or classes.

■ In addition to the chapter tests, Part 2 contains a Cumulative Diagnostic Test at the beginning and a Cumulative Mastery Test at the end. These long tests, which may be given in sections, are designed to help you evaluate your students' needs and progress.

Tests for Part 3: Academic and Workplace Skills

■ The tests for the chapters in Part 3 use multiple-choice and short answer formats to help you assess your students' mastery of the material.

Part I: Writing

**Assessment for Chapter 1:
The Writer in You**

1. Explain why writing is one of the most important skills you learn in school.

   _____

   _____

2. Circle the letter of the answer that best describes what is meant by *sentence fluency.* On the line, explain why your answer is correct.
   a. a musical quality found in writing
   b. the ability to translate writing into different languages
   c. the use of transitions and a variety of sentence structures to produce rhythm in writing
   d. the ability to write quickly and smoothly while under pressure

   _____

   _____

3. Explain the difference between the terms *voice* and *word choice.*

   _____

   _____

   _____

4. Why is it important to keep track of inspirations and ideas for writing?

   _____

   _____

5. Circle the letter of the answer that illustrates the type of writing that should be included in a style journal. On the line, explain why your answer is correct.
   a. a newspaper article
   b. a travel brochure
   c. a recipe
   d. an original poem

   _____

6. Explain how keeping a writing portfolio will assist you in becoming a better writer.

   _____

   _____

7. In the reader's journal below, jot down your observations and impressions of a story, poem, or book that you have read.

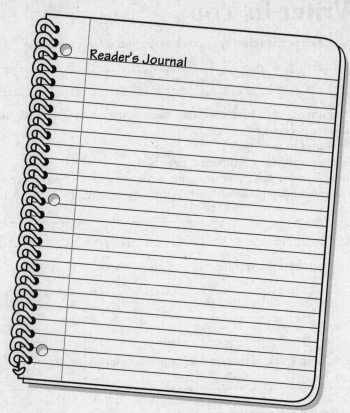

Reader's Journal

8. Which of the following is an example of prewriting? Below each answer, explain why it is correct or incorrect.
   a. changing the structure of a sentence in an essay

   _____

   b. reorganizing the order of ideas in a paragraph

   _____

   c. researching information for your topic

   _____

   d. checking the spelling and punctuation of your story

   _____

9. Explain what is meant by the idea that writing is a *recursive* process.

   _____

   Why it is important to remember this concept when you are writing?

   _____

   _____

10. Imagine that you are preparing a schedule for writing a research paper. Number the steps below so that they occur in the appropriate order. On the lines, explain why the order you selected is correct.

_____ Proofread paper.

_____ Collect data for paper through research and interviews.

_____ Brainstorm for possible topics for research.

_____ Select a topic.

_____ Create an outline.

_____ Write a draft of the paper.

_____

_____

11. List three qualities of an effective location for writing. Provide one example of a place where you would write.

_____

_____

12. How can working with others help you to improve your writing? Circle the letter of the best answer. Then, explain your answer on the line below.
    a. Other people can suggest new strategies for improving your work.
    b. Other people can tell you whether your work will be published by a magazine.
    c. Other people can tell you who will like or dislike your work.
    d. Other people can ask you for ideas about their work.

_____

13. Why is it important to avoid evaluating ideas that are expressed during a group brainstorming session?

_____

_____

14. Describe a method of group work that can assist you in the writing process.

_____

_____

15. Explain one reason that it is important for a young writer to publish his or her work.

_____

_____

16. Name one possible place for a student writer to publish his or her work.

_____

17. Give one example of why it is useful to reflect on your writing.

_____

_____

18. Which of the following questions would help you to reflect on your writing? Circle the letter of the best answer. On the line, explain why your answer is correct.
    a. What are the strong points of your writing?
    b. Why didn't you begin writing this piece earlier?
    c. Do you know any famous writers?
    d. Who assisted you with the revision of your writing?

    _____

    _____

19. Two of the professionals described in this chapter are a defense lawyer and a personal trainer. Choose one, and explain why it is important for people in this profession to write well.

    _____

    _____

20. Explain one way in which a politician can effectively use his or her writing skills.

    _____

    _____

Name ______________________ Date ____________

2 Assessment for Chapter 2: A Walk Through the Writing Process

1. Fill in the name of the type of writing that fits each definition listed below.

   The form, or shape, that writing takes, such as narration, description, or persuasion, is called ______________________.

   Writing that is from yourself and for yourself is called ______________________.

   Writing that is generated for others and intended for others is called ______________________.

2. Write the letter of the definition next to the writing stage it describes.

_______ Prewriting	a. Polishing the writing; fixing mechanics
_______ Drafting	b. Sharing your writing
_______ Revising	c. Freely exploring and choosing topics for writing
_______ Editing and Proofreading	d. Getting ideas down on paper in a rough format
_______ Publishing and Presenting	e. Correcting major errors in your writing

3. On the lines below, explain one thing the diagram shows about the writing process.

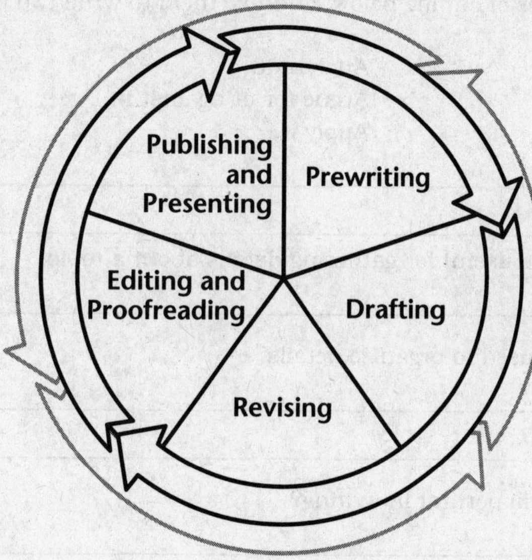

____

____

____

4. Explain why brainstorming is considered a prewriting strategy.

____

____

5. How can using a pentad help you to narrow a topic?

____

____

6. Answer the following questions about your audience, as though you were preparing to write an essay about your favorite hobby.

   What does the audience already know about my topic? _____

   _____

   What background do they need to understand my main idea? _____

   _____

   What details will interest or influence my audience? _____

   _____

7. Describe briefly the level of detail you would include for each of these audiences:

   Your peers: _____

   Your teacher: _____

   Other people who enjoy the same hobby: _____

8. Name one possible purpose for writing an essay about your favorite hobby.

   _____

   _____

9. Choose two of the examples of cubing below, and use them to write two details about your favorite hobby.

   Describe it.   Analyze it.

   Compare and contrast it.   Argue for or against it.

   Associate it.   Apply it.

   _____

   _____

   Now, explain why cubing is useful for gathering details about a topic.

   _____

10. Explain how a timeline is used to organize details.

    _____

    _____

11. Why is a powerful lead so important in writing?

    _____

    _____

12. Write a strong lead for the beginning of an autobiographical essay about your favorite hobby, using a compelling fact or an intriguing description.

    _____

    _____

Name _____

Use the passage below to answer questions 13 and 14.

> I studied hard for the geometry exam. To make sure I understood each concept, whenever I came across a concept that I was unable to grasp, I stayed after school and asked my teacher for assistance. Now that I've prepared carefully, I feel confident that I will do well.

13. Circle the letter of the statement that best reflects the main idea of the passage.
    a. Even though math is my weakest subject, I feel confident that I will do well on the final exam.
    b. I don't like math, because I'm not very good at it.
    c. Mathematics is an interesting but challenging subject.
    d. I wasn't sure if my study method would help me pass the final exam.

14. Write the extension in the passage that restates the main idea.

    _____

    Write the elaboration in the passage that provides additional details.

    _____

15. Choose the letter of the answer that contains the definition of the term *ratiocination*. Then, on the lines below, explain one way to apply this concept to revising your work.
    a. to think quickly
    b. to think logically
    c. to think slowly
    d. to think scientifically

    _____

    _____

16. Cross out the contradictory information in the paragraph below. On the line, explain why you crossed out this information.

    > Jason, my best friend, is a talented pianist. He is also a pretty good swimmer. He began playing piano when he was four years old, even though his sister didn't start until she was six. Jason was playing difficult pieces by Mozart and Beethoven by the time he was seven years old. Last year, at the age of sixteen, he gave a concert at the Performing Arts Center. Jason has a bright future as a concert pianist.

    _____

17. Now rewrite one of the sentences in the paragraph above to vary its beginning.

    _____

    _____

18. What is the purpose of a peer reviewer?

    _____

    _____

19. Give an example of a place where you might check a fact about your favorite hobby. Explain your answer.

    _____

    _____

20. Explain how a rubric can help you assess your writing.

    _____

    _____

Assessment for Chapter 3: Paragraphs and Compositions

1. Explain the difference between a paragraph and a composition.

   _____

   _____

   _____

2. Define *topic sentence*, and explain why not all paragraphs have a topic sentence.

   _____

   _____

   _____

3. Write a topic sentence for the paragraph below:

   Reference materials—such as encyclopedias, trade books, and periodicals—provide a vast source of free information. In addition, many libraries now offer Internet access and CD-ROM programs that may be used for various types of research. There is no reason that anyone should have to invest large amounts of money in research materials.

   _____

   _____

4. How would you reorganize and rewrite the information in the paragraph above so that the topic sentence may be placed at the end of the paragraph?

   _____

   _____

5. Write one sentence that would support the following topic sentence. Identify the sentence as a fact, a supporting statistic, an illustration, or a detail.

   Exercising regularly is beneficial to your overall health.

   _____

6. Write an "illustration" sentence to complete the T-R-I (Topic sentence, Restatement, Illustration) pattern of the following paragraph.

   Good reading skills are essential for school success. Students who read well have a better chance of earning higher grades or scoring higher marks on standardized tests.

   _____

   _____

7. Explain what it means for a paragraph to have unity.

   _____

   _____

   _____

8. Circle the letter of the answer that correctly completes the sentence below. On the line, explain why this choice is correct.

   A thesis statement is

   a. a sentence or two that serves as a transition between paragraphs.

   b. a sentence or two that serves to draw a conclusion about a composition.

   c. the main idea of a composition.

   d. the main idea of a paragraph.

   _____

9. Write the letter of the transition next to the appropriate type of organization.

   _____ Chronological order   a. the main reason

   _____ Spatial order   b. afterward

   _____ Order of importance   c. on the other hand

   _____ Comparison and contrast   d. behind

10. Insert appropriate transitions in the paragraph below.

    When you are writing a college essay, it is important to remember a few tips.

    _____, you should select a topic that focuses on a positive aspect of your

    experience. _____, you should narrow the focus of your topic.

    _____, if you are writing an essay that describes your experiences as a guard

    on the basketball team, you should write about your thoughts, feelings, and actions during the

    game that was most important to you. _____, pay attention to the technical

    aspects of essay writing. You need to revise so that the essay is coherent.

    _____, you should proofread to make sure it is free of mechanical errors.

    _____, you should ask someone to read your work and give you feedback.

11. Write a short paragraph that provides directions from your house to your school. Use at least three transitions.

    _____

    _____

    _____

    _____

12. Name the three parts of a composition, and explain their functions.

    _____

    _____

    _____

13. Write the following sentences for a composition about whether students should be required to do community service in order to earn a high-school diploma:

Thesis statement for introduction: _____

_____

Topic sentence for body paragraph 1: _____

_____

Topic sentence for body paragraph 2: _____

_____

Main point of conclusion: _____

_____

14. Explain the difference between a topical paragraph and a functional paragraph.

_____

_____

15. Write a three-sentence functional paragraph that can be inserted after the topical paragraph below.

I remember a certain summer storm from when I was little. My parents and I were in our mountain cabin. The gale winds wailed outside, hurling huge drops of rain against the window panes. We were sitting in front of the fireplace and becoming drowsy from the warmth of the softly glowing fire. Mother was reading my favorite bedtime story aloud, and I was dozing on and off. Eventually I fell asleep, and she carried me to my bed.

_____

_____

_____

_____

16. Circle the letter of the answer that best completes the following sentence. Explain why your answer is correct.
Paragraph blocks are useful when
a. you need to develop a single idea in more than one paragraph.
b. you need to write several topic sentences.
c. you need to compare and contrast contributing ideas.
d. you need to complicate the idea in your essay.

_____

17. Describe why sentence variety is important.

_____

18. Define the term *diction*.

_____

19. Give one example of a writing convention that is used in formal English.

_____

20. Explain whether formal or informal language should be used in each of the following examples of writing.

   a. writing a cover letter for a job application _____

   _____

   b. writing a postcard to a friend _____

   _____

   c. responding to an e-mail from your boss _____

   _____

   d. writing the script for a commercial targeted at teenagers _____

   _____

Assessment for Chapter 4: Narration: Autobiographical Writing
Test 1

In this test, you will be asked to draft an autobiographical narrative of at least three paragraphs about a memorable experience. You might write about a special trip, an amusing incident at school, or a learning experience from a summer job or volunteer project. The narrative should contain a problem or conflict. Write your topic on the line below.

_____

Prewriting

1. Describe how you will narrow your topic.

   I am writing about _____.

   I plan to focus on _____.

2. Complete the sentences below to describe a possible purpose for your narrative.
   If I am writing to INFORM, the following fact, autobiographical detail, or example will be useful:

   _____

   If I am writing to ENTERTAIN, the following funny anecdote, dialogue, or description of a character

   will be useful: _____

   _____

   If I am writing to RE-CREATE, the following sensory detail will be useful: _____

   _____

3. Gather more details about your topic by responding to the questions listed in the diagram below.

Self-Interview

1. What makes this experience/event/person special to you?_____
   _____
   _____

2. What is the one word you would choose to describe this experience/event/person?
   _____
   _____

3. Who else shared in this experience or event, or who else knew the person about whom
   you are writing? Does he or she share your feelings? Why or why not?_____
   _____
   _____

4. Did you change in any way because of this experience/event/person? Explain. _____
   _____
   _____

5. What did you learn from this experience/event/person?_____
   _____
   _____

Drafting

4. Identify the main character of your narrative, and write a sentence that describes this person.

    _____

    _____

    _____

    _____

5. Use the setting of your narrative to identify a starting point for it. Write your opening sentence on the lines below.

    _____

    _____

6. On a separate sheet of paper, use your notes and information from the graphic organizer to draft an autobiographical narrative.

7. Go back to one of your paragraphs, and write a "thought shot" for it that is composed of one sentence of dialogue.

    _____

Revising

8. Reread the ending of your draft. Think about how you can make the ending stronger by summing up your feelings or insights about the experience. Write your revised ending on the lines below.

    _____

    _____

    _____

    _____

9. Review your draft. Add a three-sentence functional paragraph to emphasize a point you made in one of your paragraphs.

    _____

    _____

    _____

    _____

10. Circle every use of the pronoun *I* in the sentences below.

    I was sure that I was going to be late. I slipped quietly into my seat, but the teacher suddenly

    turned from the chalkboard. I knew I was in trouble.

    Now, rewrite the sentences so that no two sentences in a row begin with *I*.

    _____

    _____

11. In your own narrative, locate two sentences in a row that begin with *I*, and rewrite one of them on the lines below.

    _____

    _____

Editing and Proofreading

12. Cross out each misspelled homophone in the sentences below, and write the correct spelling on the lines.

> All of the students accept me were working on there assignments. My teacher did not except the
>
> reason for my lateness, and she made it clear that it would effect my work.

_____

_____

Now, check your narrative for homophones. If you find any that are incorrect, write the correct form on the line below. If you have no homophone errors, write *none*.

_____

13. Evaluate your draft according to the rubric below. List changes that you may need to make to improve your narrative.

	Score 4	Score 3	Score 2	Score 1
Audience and Purpose	Contains details that engage the audience	Contains details appropriate for an audience	Contains few details that appeal to an audience	Is not written for a specific audience
Organization	Presents events that create an interesting narrative; told from a consistent point of view	Presents sequence of events; told from a specific point of view	Presents a confusing sequence of events; contains a point of view that is inconsistent	Presents no logical order; is told from no consistent point of view
Elaboration	Contains details that create vivid characters; contains dialogue that develops characters and plot	Contains details that develop character and describe setting; contains dialogue	Contains characters and setting; contains some dialogue	Contains few or no details to develop characters or setting; no dialogue provided
Use of Language	Uses language to create a tone; contains no errors in grammar, punctuation, or spelling	Uses vivid words; contains few errors in grammar, punctuation, and spelling	Uses clichés and trite expressions; contains some errors in grammar, punctuation, and spelling	Uses uninspired words; has many errors in grammar, punctuation, and spelling

_____

_____

_____

_____

Publishing and Presenting

14. Write the names of two people who might enjoy reading your narrative, and explain your answer.

_____

_____

15. Reflect on whether your attitude toward your topic changed as you wrote the narrative.

_____

_____

_____

Assessment for Chapter 4: Narration: Autobiographical Writing
Test 2

In this test, you will be asked to draft an autobiographical narrative of at least three paragraphs involving an encounter with another person. You might want to write about a friend, a teacher, a family member, a local shopkeeper, or a stranger. The narrative should contain a problem or conflict and reflect your relationship with the person. Write your topic on the line below.

_____

Prewriting

1. Answer the following questions to help narrow your topic.

I will focus on the following event or experience: _____.

This event or experience illustrates the following aspect of the relationship: _____
_____

2. Describe your audience and purpose for writing.

My audience is _____.

My purpose for writing is _____.

3. Gather more details about your topic by responding to the questions listed in the diagram below.

Self-Interview

1. What makes this experience/event/person special to you?_____
_____
_____

2. What is the one word you would choose to describe this experience/event/person?
_____
_____

3. Who else shared in this experience or event, or who else knew the person about whom you are writing? Does he or she share your feelings? Why or why not?_____
_____
_____

4. Did you change in any way because of this experience/event/person? Explain. _____
_____
_____

5. What did you learn from this experience/event/person?_____
_____
_____

Name _____

Drafting

4. Identify the main character in your narrative, and write a sentence that describes this person.

_____

_____

_____

_____

5. Examine the notes you have gathered on your topic. Then, on the lines below, decide whether you will start with a character, dialogue, setting, or theme. Explain your answer.

_____

_____

_____

_____

6. On a separate sheet of paper, use your notes and information from the graphic organizer to draft an autobiographical narrative.

7. As you draft your narrative, think about where you might flesh out your writing by adding dialogue. On the lines below, write one "thought shot" containing dialogue. Mark the place in your draft where you would place the "thought shot."

_____

_____

_____

Revising

8. Reread the ending of your draft. Think about how you can make the ending stronger by summing up your feelings or insights about the experience. Write your revised ending on the lines below.

_____

_____

_____

9. Read the passage below. Draw a vertical line to indicate where the topical paragraph ends and the functional paragraph begins. Then, examine your autobiographical narrative, and add a functional paragraph where one would be appropriate. Write your revision on the lines below.

"I don't understand why you don't tell me what's bothering you," I said, increasing the pace.

Daniel's silence was annoying. Suddenly, Daniel stopped in his tracks.

_____

_____

_____

10. Cross out each incorrect verb below, and write the verb in its correct tense on the line.

> Yesterday, Daniel and I went running in the park, just as we always have done. He turned to me
>
> as if he wanted to say something but suddenly changes his mind.

_____

Now, review your draft for consistency of verb tenses. If you find an unnecessary shift in tense, correct the verb, and write the corrected sentence on the line below. If you have no errors in verb tense, write *none*.

_____

_____

11. Review your sentences for connections between ideas. Look for a place where adding a transition word—such as *then, next, later,* or *finally*—will clarify a connection. Write the revised sentence on the lines.

_____

_____

Editing and Proofreading

12. Cross out each misspelled homophone in the sentences below, and write the correct spelling above it.

> I was deeply effected by the conversation I had with Daniel. As we stood their in the park, talking
>
> about the argument we had last summer, I was to overcome by my emotions to except his apology.

Now, review your draft. On the lines below, write any homophones you may have used incorrectly, and write the correct form next to them. If you have no homophone errors, write *none*.

_____

_____

13. Evaluate your draft according to the rubric below. List changes that you may need to make to improve your narrative.

	Score 4	Score 3	Score 2	Score 1
Audience and Purpose	Contains details that engage the audience	Contains details appropriate for an audience	Contains few details that appeal to an audience	Is not written for a specific audience
Organization	Presents events that create an interesting narrative; told from a consistent point of view	Presents sequence of events; told from a specific point of view	Presents a confusing sequence of events; contains a point of view that is inconsistent	Presents no logical order; is told from no consistent point of view
Elaboration	Contains details that create vivid characters; contains dialogue that develops characters and plot	Contains details that develop character and describe setting; contains dialogue	Contains characters and setting; contains some dialogue	Contains few or no details to develop characters or setting; no dialogue provided
Use of Language	Uses language to create a tone; contains no errors in grammar, punctuation, or spelling	Uses vivid words; contains few errors in grammar, punctuation, and spelling	Uses clichés and trite expressions; contains some errors in grammar, punctuation, and spelling	Uses uninspired words; has many errors in grammar, punctuation, and spelling

_____

_____

_____

_____

Publishing and Presenting

14. List two places where you might publish your autobiographical narrative.

_____

_____

15. Reflect on whether you found it more difficult to draft or to revise your narrative. Explain your answer.

_____

_____

Name _____   Date _____

Assessment for Chapter 4: Narration: Autobiographical Writing
Test 3

In this test, you will be asked to write an autobiographical narrative of about three or four paragraphs about your favorite place. Recall a place that holds special meaning, such as a room in your house, your favorite vacation spot, an area of your school, or a relative's home. The narrative should contain a problem or conflict. Write your topic on the line below.

_____

Prewriting

1. Think about why your topic is special to you. Write a sentence in which you describe the main focus you want your narrative to reveal about this place.

   _____

2. Describe your audience and purpose for the narrative.

   My audience is _____.

   My purpose for writing is _____.

3. Based on your focus, audience, and purpose, gather the details that you will need in order to convey why the place you have chosen to write about is memorable. Use the questions below to gather these details.
   What makes this place special?

   _____

   Who else knows about this place, and how does he or she feel about it?

   _____
   _____

   How did you change, or what did you learn, from being in this place?

   _____
   _____
   _____

Drafting

4. Identify the main character in your narrative, and write a sentence that describes this person.

   _____
   _____
   _____

5. Select a starting point for your narrative, based on the focus of the piece and the information that you have gathered. Write the opening sentence, and explain why you have chosen to begin your narrative in this way.

   _____
   _____
   _____

6. On a separate sheet of paper, use your notes to draft an autobiographical narrative.

7. As you write your draft, think about where you might flesh out your writing by adding dialogue. On the lines below, write one "thought shot" containing dialogue that you might include. Mark the place in your draft where you would insert the "thought shot."

_____

_____

_____

Revising

8. Reread the ending of your draft. Think about how you can make the ending stronger by summing up your feelings or insights about the experience. Write your revised ending on the lines below.

_____

_____

_____

_____

9. Read the following paragraphs, and write a functional paragraph that could serve as a transition between them. Then, examine your draft, and explain where and why you would include a functional paragraph in your narrative.

   When I was a child, I used my treehouse as a place of refuge from the stresses of daily life on our farm. There, under the cover of the large oak leaves that shaded it, I would sit in my treehouse for hours at a time, thinking about nothing in particular.
   In later years, I always regretted the fire that robbed me of this hideaway. If only I had not left the kerosene lantern burning, I would still have this place of escape today.

_____

_____

10. Circle every use of the pronoun *I* in the sentences below.

    I was startled when I awakened the next morning to the sounds of hammers and drills. I looked

    out my bedroom window. I saw my father and brother up in a tree at the edge of the yard. I ran

    outside in my pajamas to see what they were doing.

    Now, rewrite the sentences so that no two sentences in a row begin with *I*.

_____

_____

Revising

11. Write a sentence that will strengthen the connection between two of your ideas.

_____

Editing and Proofreading

12. Cross out each misspelled homophone in the sentences below, and write the correct spelling above it.

    For a moment, I was to shocked to speak, unable to except what I saw. They're they were, my fa-

    ther and brother, building a new treehouse for me!

    Now, on the line below, write any homophones you may have used incorrectly in your narrative, and write the correct form next to them. If you have no errors, write *none*.

_____

Name _____

13. Evaluate your draft according to the rubric below. Write changes that you may need to make to improve your narrative.

	Score 4	Score 3	Score 2	Score 1
Audience and Purpose	Contains details that engage the audience	Contains details appropriate for an audience	Contains few details that appeal to an audience	Is not written for a specific audience
Organization	Presents events that create an interesting narrative; told from a consistent point of view	Presents sequence of events; told from a specific point of view	Presents a confusing sequence of events; contains a point of view that is inconsistent	Presents no logical order; is told from no consistent point of view
Elaboration	Contains details that create vivid characters; contains dialogue that develops characters and plot	Contains details that develop character and describe setting; contains dialogue	Contains characters and setting; contains some dialogue	Contains few or no details to develop characters or setting; no dialogue provided
Use of Language	Uses language to create a tone; contains no errors in grammar, punctuation, or spelling	Uses vivid words; contains few errors in grammar, punctuation, and spelling	Uses clichés and trite expressions; contains some errors in grammar, punctuation, and spelling	Uses uninspired words; has many errors in grammar, punctuation, and spelling

_____

_____

_____

_____

Publishing and Presenting

14. Describe the kind of publication that might be interested in publishing an autobiographical narrative such as yours.

_____

_____

15. Reflect upon the stage of the writing process that you found most challenging.

_____

_____

Assessment for Chapter 5:
Narration: Short Story
Test 1

In this test, you will be asked to write a short story of at least five paragraphs. Identify a real-life event to spark an idea. Consider an event in the news, a school situation, or an overheard conversation. Then, build on this idea by developing the plot, characters, and a conflict for your story. Write the subject of your story on the lines.

_____

_____

Prewriting

1. Answer the questions presented in the diagram below in order to develop a specific focus for your story.

Character	Who is your main character? What does he or she want? _____ _____ _____
Adjectives to describe character	What type of person is your main character? _____ _____
Setting	When and where does your story take place? _____ _____
Problem (conflict)	What does your character want? What is preventing him or her from getting it? _____ _____
Actions (plot)	What does your character do to get what he or she wants? What happens as a result? _____ _____
Resolution	How do things finally turn out? _____ _____

2. Think about whether you want your audience to laugh, cry, learn something important, or see things in a new way. What is the purpose of your story, and what details can you include to achieve that purpose?

_____

_____

_____

Name _____

3. Give one example of how you might capture details about characters or setting for your story.

_____

_____

Drafting

4. Briefly note one or more details that you will include for each plot element.

Exposition: _____

Rising action: _____

Climax: _____

Falling action: _____

Resolution: _____

5. How might you intensify the conflict in your story?

_____

_____

6. Use the SEE method below to help you develop the plot.
Write a statement that conveys a basic idea in your story.

_____

Write an extension to explain or define the statement above.

_____

Write an elaboration that gives more information about the statement.

_____

7. On a separate sheet of paper, use the notes and information from the graphic organizer to draft your short story.

Revising

8. Write a sentence or a line of dialogue that you can add near the beginning of your draft to foreshadow an event that occurs later in the story.

_____

9. Read the paragraph below and reorganize it into separate, functional paragraphs that begin each time a new character speaks.

"Well, I suppose there is no reason to go any farther," John remarked after he surveyed the road-

block. "Are you sure we can't drive around it?" Joe asked. "Positive."

_____

_____

_____

_____

_____

_____

10. Review your draft. Mark a place where a functional paragraph could emphasize a point or make a transition. Write a three-sentence functional paragraph below.

_____

_____

_____

_____

11. Read the sentences below, and rewrite them to vary their beginnings or their length.

Joe stared at the roadblock. He stared for a long time. He wondered whether they would be able to drive around it. He decided that John was right.

_____

_____

_____

_____

_____

Now, examine your draft to see where variety in sentence length or beginnings is needed. Rewrite one of those sentences on the lines below. If no such revision is needed, write *none*.

_____

_____

Editing and Proofreading

12. Rewrite the dialogue below, punctuating it correctly.

Do you think we should ask the police for assistance Joe asked

After a moment's thought, Brian said we could try

Anyway Joe concluded we should give it a shot

Now, review your draft. Correct any errors in the punctuation of dialogue. Write one example of corrected dialogue on the lines below. If you do not find any errors, write *none*.

_____

_____

_____

_____

13. Evaluate your draft according to the rubric below. List changes that you may need to make to improve your short story.

	Score 4	Score 3	Score 2	Score 1
Audience and Purpose	Contains details that create a tone to engage the audience	Contains details and language that appeal to an audience	Contains few details that contribute to its purpose or appeal to an audience	Contains no purpose; is not written for a specific audience
Organization	Presents events that create an interesting, clear narrative; told from a consistent point of view	Presents sequence of events; told from a specific point of view	Presents a confusing sequence of events; contains inconsistent points of view	Presents no logical order; is told from no consistent point of view
Elaboration	Contains details that provide insight into character; contains dialogue that reveals characters and furthers the plot	Contains details and dialogue that develop character	Contains characters and setting; contains some dialogue	Contains few or no details to develop characters or setting; no dialogue provided
Use of Language	Uses word choice and tone to reveal story's theme; contains no errors in grammar, punctuation, or spelling	Uses interesting and fresh word choices; contains few errors in grammar, punctuation, and spelling	Uses clichés and trite expressions; contains some errors in grammar, punctuation, and spelling	Uses uninspired word choices; has many errors in grammar, punctuation, and spelling

_____
_____
_____
_____

Publishing and Presenting

14. Describe how you would make your short story more exciting if you were to read it aloud.

_____
_____
_____

15. What did you learn about your writing skills as you wrote this story?

_____
_____
_____

Assessment for Chapter 5: Narration: Short Story
Test 2

In this test, you will be asked to write a futuristic science-fiction story of at least five paragraphs. Base your story on a conflict involving an advanced form of technology involved in communication, medicine, or space travel. Write your topic on the line below.

_____

Prewriting

1. Answer the questions presented in the diagram below in order to focus your story.

Character	Who is your main character? What does he or she want? _____ _____ _____
Adjectives to describe character	What type of person is your main character? _____ _____
Setting	When and where does your story take place? _____ _____
Problem (conflict)	What does your character want? What is preventing him or her from getting it? _____ _____
Actions (plot)	What does your character do to get what he or she wants? What happens as a result? _____ _____
Resolution	How do things finally turn out? _____ _____

2. Think about whether you want your audience to laugh, cry, learn something important, or see things in a new way. What is the purpose of your story, and what details can you include to achieve that purpose?

_____

_____

3. Give one example of how you might capture details about characters or setting for your story.

_____

_____

Drafting

4. Briefly note one or more details that you will include for each plot element.

   Exposition: _____

   Rising action: _____

   Climax: _____

   Falling action: _____

   Resolution: _____

5. How do you plan to intensify the conflict in your story? _____

   _____

6. Use the SEE method below to help you develop the plot.

   Write a statement that conveys a basic idea in your story. _____

   _____

   Write an extension to explain or define the statement above.

   _____

   _____

   Write an elaboration that gives more information about the statement.

   _____

   _____

7. On a separate sheet of paper, use the notes and information from the graphic organizer to draft your short story.

Revising

8. Read the excerpt below and, at an appropriate point, insert a sentence that foreshadows a later event in the story.

   > Juanita opened the door slowly. She walked over to the small table beside the bed, took the book that lay there, and slipped it into her computer case.

   Now, to build suspense, write a line that foreshadows an event in your own story.

   _____

9. Read the paragraph below, and break it into separate, functional paragraphs that begin each time a new character speaks.

   > "Who is that man?" Juanita wondered. "Do you recognize him?" Maria asked. "I'm not sure."

   _____

   _____

   _____

10. Review your draft. Find a place where a functional paragraph could emphasize a point or make a transition. Mark the place in your manuscript where you would make the insertion. Then, write the functional paragraph below.

   _____

   _____

   _____

11. Read the sentences below, and rewrite them to vary their beginnings or their length.

   > Juanita slipped quietly onto the electric walkway. Juanita was amidst a crowd of people. They were all talking into their videophone wristbands. They did not notice her.

   _____

   _____

   _____

   _____

   Now, examine your draft to see where variation in sentence length or sentence beginnings is needed. Rewrite one of those sentences on the lines below. If no such revision is needed, write *none*.

   _____

   _____

   _____

Editing and Proofreading

12. Correct the punctuation in the dialogue below.

   > Juanita said "that she felt tired."
   >
   > Oh, really? Marcus asked. And why is that?
   >
   > I don't know, Juanita answered Maybe I'm getting a cold.

   Now, review your draft for errors in the punctuation of dialogue. Write one example of corrected dialogue on the lines below. If you have no errors in punctuating dialogue, write *none*.

   _____

   _____

13. Evaluate your draft according to the rubric below. List any changes that you may need to make to improve your short story.

	Score 4	Score 3	Score 2	Score 1
Audience and Purpose	Contains details that create a tone to engage the audience	Contains details and language that appeal to an audience	Contains few details that contribute to its purpose or appeal to an audience	Contains no purpose; is not written for a specific audience
Organization	Presents events that create an interesting, clear narrative; told from a consistent point of view	Presents sequence of events; told from a specific point of view	Presents a confusing sequence of events; contains inconsistent points of view	Presents no logical order; is told from no consistent point of view
Elaboration	Contains details that provide insight into character; contains dialogue that reveals characters and furthers the plot	Contains details and dialogue that develop character	Contains characters and setting; contains some dialogue	Contains few or no details to develop characters or setting; no dialogue provided
Use of Language	Uses word choice and tone to reveal story's theme; contains no errors in grammar, punctuation, or spelling	Uses interesting and fresh word choices; contains few errors in grammar, punctuation, and spelling	Uses clichés and trite expressions; contains some errors in grammar, punctuation, and spelling	Uses uninspired word choices; has many errors in grammar, punctuation, and spelling

_____

_____

_____

_____

Publishing and Presenting

14. Would you want to try to submit your short story to a literary contest? Why or why not?

_____

_____

15. What advice might you give to someone who is preparing to write a short story?

_____

_____

_____

_____

Assessment for Chapter 5:
Narration: Short Story
Test 3

In this test, you will be asked to write a fable or a folk tale of at least three paragraphs. Consider a story that explains why a natural event occurs, a story that presents a real-life character as larger-than-life or exaggerates the person's heroism, or a story that explains human beings' relationship to nature or outer space. Write your topic on the line below.

_____

Prewriting

1. Answer the questions in the diagram below in order to focus your story.

Character	Who is your main character? What does he or she want? _____ _____ _____
Adjectives to describe character	What type of person is your main character? _____ _____
Setting	When and where does your story take place? _____ _____
Problem (conflict)	What does your character want? What is preventing him or her from getting it? _____ _____
Actions (plot)	What does your character do to get what he or she wants? What happens as a result? _____ _____
Resolution	How do things finally turn out? _____ _____

2. Think about whether you want your audience to laugh, cry, learn something important, or see things in a new way. What is the purpose of your story, and how will you attempt to achieve your purpose?

_____

_____

_____

3. Give one example of how you might capture details about characters and setting for your story.

_____

_____

Name _____

Drafting

4. Briefly note one or more details that you will include for each plot element.

   Exposition: _____

   Rising action: _____

   Climax: _____

   Falling action: _____

   Resolution: _____

5. How might you intensify the conflict in your story? _____
   _____

6. Use the SEE method below to help you develop the plot.

   Write a statement that conveys a basic idea in your story. _____
   _____

   Write an extension to explain or define the statement above. _____
   _____

   Write an elaboration that gives more information about the statement. _____
   _____

7. On a separate sheet of paper, use the notes and information from the graphic organizer to draft your short story.

Revising

8. To build suspense, write a sentence or line of dialogue near the beginning of your story that foreshadows a later event.
   _____
   _____

9. Review your draft. Find a place where a functional paragraph could emphasize a point or make a transition. Mark the place in your manuscript where you would make the insert. Then, write the functional paragraph below.

   _____
   _____
   _____

10. Rewrite the following dialogue so that the language used by the characters suits their relationship to each other. Explain why you changed the language.

> "Hey, Private Reynolds, how's it going?" General Hayes asked.
>
> "Everything's okay," Private Reynolds responded. "What's up with you, General?"
>
> "Nothing much," the General answered.

_____

_____

_____

_____

Now, examine your draft and, if necessary, revise dialogue so that it suits the relationship between two characters. On the lines below, write one example of revised dialogue. If you find no such errors, write *none*.

_____

_____

_____

_____

11. Review your draft for a place where you can make the dialogue sound more natural by using a partial sentence, a contraction, or slang. Write an example of one such revision on the lines below.

_____

_____

Editing and Proofreading

12. Rewrite the dialogue below so that it is correctly punctuated.

> Don't worry the Captain said, We'll get through this storm.
>
> How? asked the first mate. Our main sail is torn, and we're taking on water.
>
> The Captain assured his crew that he would find a way to get them to land safely.

Now, review your draft. Correct any errors in the punctuation of dialogue on the lines below. If you do not find any errors, write *none*.

_____

_____

_____

_____

Name _____

13. Evaluate your draft according to the rubric below. List any changes that you may need to make to improve your short story.

	Score 4	Score 3	Score 2	Score 1
Audience and Purpose	Contains details that create a tone to engage the audience	Contains details and language that appeal to an audience	Contains few details that contribute to its purpose or appeal to an audience	Contains no purpose; is not written for a specific audience
Organization	Presents events that create an interesting, clear narrative; told from a consistent point of view	Presents sequence of events; told from a specific point of view	Presents a confusing sequence of events; contains inconsistent points of view	Presents no logical order; is told from no consistent point of view
Elaboration	Contains details that provide insight into character; contains dialogue that reveals characters and furthers the plot	Contains details and dialogue that develop character	Contains characters and setting; contains some dialogue	Contains few or no details to develop characters or setting; no dialogue provided
Use of Language	Uses word choice and tone to reveal story's theme; contains no errors in grammar, punctuation, or spelling	Uses interesting and fresh word choices; contains few errors in grammar, punctuation, and spelling	Uses clichés and trite expressions; contains some errors in grammar, punctuation, and spelling	Uses uninspired word choices; has many errors in grammar, punctuation, and spelling

_____

_____

_____

Publishing and Presenting

14. Explain the special visual and sound effects you would use if you were to film your story.

_____

_____

15. Reflect on one thing you learned about yourself as a writer while you wrote this short story.

_____

_____

Assessment for Chapter 6: Description
Test 1

In this test, you will be asked to write a descriptive essay of at least three paragraphs about an event that you have observed. Consider an athletic competition, a parade, or a phenomenon of nature, such as a sunrise. Write your topic on the line below.

_____

Prewriting

1. Narrow your topic by sketching the event to help you bring details into focus.

2. Describe your audience and your purpose for writing.

   My audience is _____.

   My purpose for writing is _____.

3. Based on the information that you have gathered, use the chart below to generate sensory details about your topic.

SIGHT	HEARING	SMELL	TASTE	TOUCH

Drafting

4. Think about your topic, purpose for writing, and audience. Then, complete the following sentences.

   Using a first-person point of view would help me to _____.

   Using a third-person point of view would help me to _____.

5. Name the point of view that you have decided to use for your descriptive essay, and explain your choice.

_____

_____

6. On a separate sheet of paper, use your notes and information from the graphic organizer to draft a descriptive essay.

7. As you draft, pause at the end of a paragraph, and use the "depth-charging" strategy. Write a sentence that is an important part of the description, using a sense other than sight.

_____

In a second sentence, expand on a detail from the sentence you just wrote, using a different sense.

_____

Write a third sentence using another detail from the sentence you just wrote, using a third, different sense.

_____

Revising

8. Describe the dominant impression that you are trying to give to your audience.

_____

Underline any details in your draft that do not directly convey this impression. Write one example below. If you have no details that detract from the dominant impression, write *none*.

_____

9. Read the following paragraph. Underline the topic sentence, and cross out any sentence that does not support the topic sentence.

As I sat on the bench, I watched the sun rise over the ocean. At first, there was little more than a pink glow over the horizon. The sea gulls began their noisy conversation. Then, the fiery orange ball inched its way up into the sky, sending ripples of light across the ocean waves. As the sun climbed higher into the sky, I felt the comforting warmth of its rays on my upturned face.

Now, review the topic sentence of each topical paragraph in your draft. Underline any sentences that do not support the topic sentence, and write one example below. If you do not find any such sentences in your draft, write *none*.

_____

_____

10. Rewrite the following sentences, turning one of them into an appositive.

The players took their positions on the field. My brother stood on his seat in order to get a glimpse of one of his favorite stars. There he was. It was Mickey Mantle.

_____

_____

_____

Now, review your draft, looking for a place where you might combine two sentences by turning one of them into an appositive. Write your revision on the lines.

_____

_____

11. Mark a place in your draft where you can further identify or explain your topic. Write the added details on the line.

_____

Editing and Proofreading

12. Underline the appositives in each sentence below. If the appositive is nonessential, add commas where needed.

Last week, the mystery writer Sue Grafton came to New York to accept a literary award. After the

award ceremony, Ms. Grafton ate at Lindy's a restaurant famous for its cheesecake.

Now, review your draft for appositives, and check to see that they are punctuated correctly. Write one example of a correction below. If you have no errors in punctuating appositives, write *none*.

_____

_____

13. Evaluate your draft according to the rubric below. List any changes that you may need to make in your essay.

	Score 4	Score 3	Score 2	Score 1
Audience and Purpose	Contains details that work together to create a single, dominant impression of the topic	Creates through use of details a dominant impression of the topic	Contains extraneous details that detract from the main impression	Contains details that are unfocused and create no dominant impression
Organization	Is organized consistently, logically, and effectively	Is organized consistently	Is organized, but not consistently	Is disorganized and confusing
Elaboration	Contains creative use of descriptive details	Contains many descriptive details	Contains some descriptive details	Contains no descriptive details
Use of Language	Contains sensory language that appeals to the five senses; contains no errors in grammar, punctuation, or spelling	Contains some sensory language; contains few errors in grammar, punctuation, and spelling	Contains some sensory language, but it appeals to only one or two of the senses; contains some errors in grammar, punctuation, and spelling	Contains no sensory language; contains many errors in grammar, punctuation, and spelling

_____

_____

_____

Publishing and Presenting

14. Explain how you would illustrate your descriptive essay.

_____

_____

15. Reflect on the advice you would give to someone who was planning to write a description.

_____

_____

6

Assessment for Chapter 6: Description
Test 2

In this test, you will be asked to write a descriptive essay of at least three paragraphs about a place—a room, an outdoor location, a town or city, a workplace, or a vacation spot. Write your topic on the line below.

_____

Prewriting

1. Narrow your topic by sketching the place that you would like to describe.

2. Identify your audience and your purpose for writing.

   My audience is _____.

   My purpose for writing is _____

   _____.

3. Use the chart below to generate sensory details about your topic.

SIGHT	HEARING	SMELL	TASTE	TOUCH

Drafting

4. Will you use a first-person or third-person point of view? Explain your choice.

   _____

5. What point of view have you decided to use for your descriptive essay? Explain your choice.

_____

_____

6. On a separate sheet of paper, use your notes and information from the graphic organizer to draft a descriptive essay.

7. Read the excerpt below. For each underlined word, use the "depth-charging" strategy to write a sentence that elaborates on the word.

> I go to the park after a difficult day. The green shade of the oak trees, the chirping of the birds, and the solitary pathways create an atmosphere that allows me to reflect on the day's events and become calmer.

_____

_____

Then, as you draft, circle two key words that you want to elaborate on, and write sentences that do so.

_____

_____

Revising

8. Circle the details in the paragraph below that create a dominant impression. Cross out the ones that do not contribute to a dominant impression.

> Smith Park is an oasis of calm located between two major highways. These highways are usually packed with cars. The branches of the tall oak trees spread out to form a green canopy that shields me from the noise. Most of these cars emit a large amount of exhaust fumes. The tingly scent of the cedar trees soothes my jangled nerves.

_____

_____

9. Describe the dominant impression that you are trying to give to your audience.

_____

If you find any details that do not directly convey this impression, write them below. If you have no details that detract from the dominant impression, write none.

_____

10. Rewrite the following sentences, adding two appositives in the appropriate places.

> The birds fly overhead. A squirrel hunts for nuts near my feet. Wherever I look, the park is alive.

_____

_____

Now, review your draft. Find a sentence where you could add appositives. Write the new sentence.

_____

11. Add one sentence that includes more sensory details.

_____

Name _____

Editing and Proofreading

12. Underline the appositives in each sentence below. Then, write "E" above essential appositives and "N" above nonessential appositives. Add commas where needed.

> The writer Pearl S. Buck warned about abusing nature in her novel *Silent Spring*. This book once a bestseller is now largely overlooked on school reading lists.

Now, review your draft. Correct the punctuation that is used to set off appositives. Write the corrections below. If you do not find any errors in punctuation, write *none*.

_____

_____

13. Evaluate your draft according to the rubric below. List any changes that you may need to make to improve your essay.

	Score 4	Score 3	Score 2	Score 1
Audience and Purpose	Contains details that work together to create a single, dominant impression of the topic	Creates through use of details a dominant impression of the topic	Contains extraneous details that detract from the main impression	Contains details that are unfocused and create no dominant impression
Organization	Is organized consistently, logically, and effectively	Is organized consistently	Is organized, but not consistently	Is disorganized and confusing
Elaboration	Contains creative use of descriptive details	Contains many descriptive details	Contains some descriptive details	Contains no descriptive details
Use of Language	Contains sensory language that appeals to the five senses; contains no errors in grammar, punctuation, or spelling	Contains some sensory language; contains few errors in grammar, punctuation, and spelling	Contains some sensory language, but it appeals to only one or two of the senses; contains some errors in grammar, punctuation, and spelling	Contains no sensory language; contains many errors in grammar, punctuation, and spelling

_____

_____

_____

_____

Publishing and Presenting

14. List two local publications that might be interested in your descriptive essay.

_____

15. Did you find sketching a useful way to help you narrow your topic? Why or why not?

_____

_____

Assessment for Chapter 6: Description
Test 3

In this test, you will be asked to write a descriptive essay of at least four paragraphs about a person. Consider your best friend, a teacher, a family member, a local shopkeeper, or a celebrity. Write your topic on the line below.

_____

Prewriting

1. Narrow your topic by sketching a specific part of the experience that you would like to write about.

2. Describe your audience and your purpose for writing.

   My audience is _____.

   My purpose for writing is _____.
   Now, write a phrase of description with word choices that help to support your purpose.

   _____

3. Based on the information that you have gathered, use the chart below to generate sensory details about your topic.

SIGHT	HEARING	SMELL	TASTE	TOUCH

Drafting

4. Think about the topic, purpose for writing, and your audience. Then, complete the following sentences.

   Using a first-person point of view would help me to _____.

   Using a third-person point of view would help me to _____.

5. Describe the point of view that you have decided to use for your descriptive essay, and explain your choice.

   _____

   _____

6. On a separate sheet of paper, use your notes and information from the graphic organizer to draft a descriptive essay.

7. As you draft, pause and use the "depth-charging" strategy to add a sentence to each paragraph.

   _____

   _____

   _____

   _____

Revising

8. Underline the topic sentence in the paragraph below. On the lines provided, explain where else the topic sentence could be placed. Explain how the movement of the topic sentence changes the effect of the paragraph.

   My grandmother's ability to tell a good story reflected an innate gift. She knew exactly how to

   create suspense, paint a picture with words, and imitate conversations of the people involved so that

   we would burst with laughter. Every story she told was full of real-life details. Grandma's storytelling

   ability was even more remarkable to me because she was completely unable to read or write.

   _____

   _____

   _____

   Now, examine your draft, and select one paragraph in which you change the position of the topic sentence. Explain how this change of position affects the paragraph in your draft.

   _____

   _____

   _____

9. Combine the two sentences below by making one an appositive.

Sarah Billings taught art at Stevens Elementary School. She was the youngest member of the

staff.

_____

_____

_____

Now, review your draft for two sentences that might be combined by making one an appositive. If you can make such a revison, write the new sentence below; otherwise, write *none*.

_____

10. Consider the tone of your essay. Revise words that do not reflect that tone. Write the old and new words below. If no words need to be changed, write *none*.

_____

_____

11. Add a sentence to strengthen the dominant impression you are trying to achieve in your essay. Mark the place in your draft where you would insert the sentence.

_____

_____

Editing and Proofreading

12. Underline the appositives in each sentence below. Add commas where needed.

Jane my sister is vacationing in Los Angeles. She intends to visit Magnificent Films Studios the site

where many of her favorite movies were made. When she returns. Jane plans to read the book *The*

Making of MFS.

Now, review your draft for appositives. Correct any that are incorrectly punctuated. Write one example of a correction below. If you do not find any errors in punctuating appositives, write *none*.

_____

_____

13. Evaluate your draft according to the rubric below. List any changes that you may need to make to improve your essay.

	Score 4	Score 3	Score 2	Score 1
Audience and Purpose	Contains details that work together to create a single, dominant impression of the topic	Creates through use of details a dominant impression of the topic	Contains extraneous details that detract from the main impression	Contains details that are unfocused and create no dominant impression
Organization	Is organized consistently, logically, and effectively	Is organized consistently	Is organized, but not consistently	Is disorganized and confusing
Elaboration	Contains creative use of descriptive details	Contains many descriptive details	Contains some descriptive details	Contains no descriptive details
Use of Language	Contains sensory language that appeals to the five senses; contains no errors in grammar, punctuation, or spelling	Contains some sensory language; contains few errors in grammar, punctuation, and spelling	Contains some sensory language, but it appeals to only one or two of the senses; contains some errors in grammar, punctuation, and spelling	Contains no sensory language; contains many errors in grammar, punctuation, and spelling

_____

_____

_____

Publishing and Presenting

14. Explain which part of your descriptive essay would benefit from an illustration.

_____

_____

15. How did making a sketch help you to narrow your topic? Is there another method you find more useful?

_____

_____

_____

Assessment for Chapter 7: Persuasion: Persuasive Speech
Test 1

In this test, you will be asked to write a persuasive speech of at least three paragraphs on a controversial issue. Here are ideas you might consider:

1) Should the school day or the school year be longer (or shorter)?
2) Are there enough study areas in the school?
3) Should community service be a requirement for graduation?

Write your topic on the line below.

_____

Prewriting

1. Use the outline below to assist you in narrowing your topic. You may need to keep dividing your topic into smaller parts to narrow your topic sufficiently. Circle the section of the outline that represents the narrowed topic on which you will base your speech.

   I. School Issues _____

       A. _____

          1. _____

          2. _____

       B. _____

          1. _____

          2. _____

2. Identify the purpose of your speech.

   My general purpose is _____.

   My specific purpose is _____.

3. Use the T-chart below to gather two points for, and two points against, your topic.

For	Against

Drafting

4. Focus on your persuasive appeal by writing a precise and emphatic statement to open your speech, paying attention to how the words will sound when they are read aloud.

_____

_____

5. Write a concluding sentence for your speech that will present your most attractive and direct appeal.

   _____
   _____

6. Use the SEE method to create an effective paragraph for your draft.

   Write a statement that conveys the topic of the paragraph.

   _____

   Write an extension to explain or define the statement above.

   _____

   Write an elaboration that gives more information about the statement and supports it.

   _____

7. On a separate sheet of paper, use your notes and information from the graphic organizer to draft a persuasive speech.

Revising

8. On the lines below, create an outline of your draft. Then, cross out the information that does not directly support your position or is not directly related to your topic. If you do not need to cross out any information, write *none*.

   _____
   _____
   _____
   _____
   _____
   _____

9. Cross out the word or phrase below that is not parallel with the others. Rewrite it so that it is parallel.

   Joe mowed the lawn, raked the leaves, and then he went to take out the garbage.

   _____

   There are three areas that you need to cover in your paper: economy, culture, and how the children are educated.

   _____

   Now, examine your draft for use of parallel structure. Note where you can add or revise a sentence to introduce parallel structure and create an ear-catching rhythm. Write the new or revised sentence on the line.

   _____

10. Find two empty phrases or hedging words in your draft, and rewrite them below. Examples of empty phrases are *needless to say*, *it is a fact that*, and *the thing is*. Examples of hedging words are *somewhat*, *quite*, and *sort of*.

    _____
    _____

11. Add a sentence that will strengthen the connection between two of your ideas.

    _____

Editing and Proofreading

12. Cross out any misspelled homophones in the sentences below. Above each misspelling, write the correct word.

> We must not except a lower offer for the school property. Even though we are in a weaker posi-
>
> tion then our rivals, we must work hard to lobby our supporters. While the city counsel's intention in
>
> selling the property is good, the affects of selling it for such a low price would be disastrous.

Now, examine your draft. Correct any misspelled homophones on the lines below. If you have no misspelled homophones, write *none*.

_____

13. Evaluate your draft according to the rubric below. List any changes that you may need to make to improve your speech.

	Score 4	Score 3	Score 2	Score 1
Audience and Purpose	Chooses highly effective words; clearly focuses on persuasive task	Chooses effective words; focuses on persuasive task	Occasionally uses effective words; is minimally focused on persuasive task	Poor word choice shows lack of attention to persuasive task
Organization	Uses clear, consistent organizational strategy	Uses clear organizational strategy with occasional inconsistencies	Uses inconsistent organizational strategy and illogical presentation	Lacks organizational strategy; gives confusing presentation
Elaboration	Contains specific, well-elaborated reasons that provide convincing support for the writer's position	Contains two or more moderately elaborated reasons in support of the writer's position	Contains several reasons, but few are elaborated	Contains no specific reasons
Use of Language	Contains no empty or hedging words; makes no errors in grammar, spelling, and punctuation	Contains few empty or hedging words; makes few errors in grammar, spelling, and punctuation	Contains some empty and hedging words; makes errors in grammar, spelling, and punctuation	Contains many empty or hedging words; makes many errors in grammar, spelling, and punctuation

_____

_____

_____

_____

Publishing and Presenting

14. Describe another audience that would be appropriate for your speech.

_____

15. Reflect on some techniques you have learned that helped you to write persuasively.

_____

_____

Assessment for Chapter 7: Persuasion: Persuasive Speech
Test 2

In this test, you will be asked to write a persuasive speech of at least three paragraphs on a controversial issue. Consider one of the following ideas:

1) Should curfews be imposed on teenagers?
2) Should the driving age be raised to eighteen?
3) Should the hours that teens work during the school year be limited?

Write your topic on the line below.

_____

Prewriting

1. Use the outline below to assist you in narrowing your topic. You may need to keep dividing your topic into smaller parts to narrow your topic sufficiently. Circle the section of the outline that represents the narrowed topic on which you will base your speech.

   I. School Issues _____

      A. _____

         1. _____

         2. _____

      B. _____

         1. _____

         2. _____

2. Identify the purpose of your speech.

   My general purpose is _____

   My specific purpose is _____

3. Use the T-chart below to gather two points for, and two points against, your topic.

For	Against

Drafting

4. Focus on your persuasive appeal by writing a precise and emphatic statement to open your speech, paying attention to how the words will sound when they are read aloud.

   _____

   _____

   Write a concluding sentence for your speech that will present your most attractive and direct appeal.

   _____

5. Read the passage below. Using the layering approach, add necessary information.

   > First of all, imposing a curfew would sharply limit teenagers' ability to hold part-time jobs during the school year. Many teens work hours that extend beyond an eight o'clock curfew.

   _____

   _____

6. Use the SEE method to create an effective paragraph for your draft.
   Write a statement that conveys the topic of the paragraph.

   _____

   Write an extension to explain or define the statement above.

   _____

   Write an elaboration that gives more information about the statement and supports it.

   _____

7. On a separate sheet of paper, use your notes and information from the graphic organizer to draft a persuasive speech.

Revising

8. Find a sentence in your draft that does not contribute to its unity. Write it below.

   _____

9. Cross out the word or phrase below that does not have parallelism. Rewrite it below in a parallel structure.

   > Imposing a curfew will have a negative impact on teenagers. They will be unable to work. Studying long hours at a friend's house will be out of the question. Finally, a curfew prevents teens from participating in community service activities. Teens will have to depend on adults for what they could formerly provide for themselves.

   _____

   _____

   _____

   _____

   Now, examine your draft. Rewrite one sentence in a parallel structure to create an ear-catching rhythm.

   _____

10. Find two empty phrases or hedging words in your draft, and rewrite them below. Examples of empty phrases are *needless to say, it is a fact that,* and *the thing is.* Examples of hedging words are *in a way, kind of,* and *sort of.*

   _____

   _____

11. Add a sentence containing an argument that will strengthen your position.

   _____

   _____

Editing and Proofreading

12. Cross out any misspelled homophones in the sentences below. Above each misspelling, write the correct word.

   The committee did not except his application, but there rejection did not effect Frank's spirits. He

   new that he would find a good job soon.

   Now, examine your draft. Correct any misspelled homophones on the lines below. If you have no misspelled homophones, write *none.*

   _____

13. Evaluate your draft according to the rubric below. List any changes that you may need to make to improve your speech.

	Score 4	Score 3	Score 2	Score 1
Audience and Purpose	Chooses highly effective words; clearly focuses on persuasive task	Chooses effective words; focuses on persuasive task	Occasionally uses effective words; is minimally focused on persuasive task	Poor word choice shows lack of attention to persuasive task
Organization	Uses clear, consistent organizational strategy	Uses clear organizational strategy with occasional inconsistencies	Uses inconsistent organizational strategy and illogical presentation	Lacks organizational strategy; gives confusing presentation
Elaboration	Contains specific, well-elaborated reasons that provide convincing support for the writer's position	Contains two or more moderately elaborated reasons in support of the writer's position	Contains several reasons, but few are elaborated	Contains no specific reasons
Use of Language	Contains no empty or hedging words; makes no errors in grammar, spelling, and punctuation	Contains few empty or hedging words; makes few errors in grammar, spelling, and punctuation	Contains some empty and hedging words; makes errors in grammar, spelling, and punctuation	Contains many empty or hedging words; makes many errors in grammar, spelling, and punctuation

   _____

   _____

   _____

   _____

   _____

Publishing and Presenting

14. List two key points of your speech, and explain how you would emphasize them if you were to present the speech.

_____

_____

_____

_____

15. Reflect on the aspects of the topic you learned more about as you were writing the speech.

_____

_____

_____

_____

**Assessment for Chapter 7:
Persuasion: Persuasive Speech**
Test 3

In this test, you will be asked to write a persuasive speech of at least five paragraphs on an issue dealing with current events. Consider the following ideas: how to encourage more students to continue their education, whether to spend more money on education, or whether there are real-world topics that should be added to the current curriculum. Write your topic on the line below.

_____

Prewriting

1. Create an outline in which you divide your topic into smaller subtopics. After you have finished this outline, circle the part on which you will base your speech.

   _____

   _____

   _____

   _____

   _____

2. Identify both the general and specific purposes of your speech.

   My general purpose is _____

   My specific purpose is _____

3. Use the T-chart below to gather three points for, and three points against, your topic.

For	Against

Drafting

4. Focus on your persuasive appeal by writing a precise and emphatic statement to open your speech. Pay attention to how the words will sound when they are read aloud.

   _____

   _____

   Write a concluding sentence for your speech that will present your most direct appeal.

   _____

5. Read the passage below. Use the layering approach to add necessary information.

> Existing school buildings were designed to accommodate far fewer students. Therefore, the present boom in the student population has strained the capacity of these facilities to hold them.

_____

_____

Now, explain why the information you added is appropriate.

_____

6. Use the SEE method to create an effective paragraph for your draft.

Statement: _____

Extension: _____

Elaboration: _____

7. On a separate sheet of paper, use your notes and information from the graphic organizer to draft a persuasive speech.

Revising

8. Examine your draft. Rewrite one paragraph in a parallel structure to help listeners stay focused and attentive.

_____

_____

_____

_____

_____

9. Cross out the empty phrases and hedging words below.

> Lastly, as I said before, it is also true that overcrowded schools make it difficult for students to learn. Larger classes make it kind of difficult for students to receive proper attention from their teachers. Needless to say, it seems as if some students may fall through the cracks and not receive the necessary assistance that they need to continue their academic progress.

_____

_____

Now, review your draft. Find two sentences with empty phrases or hedging words, and correct them below.

_____

_____

10. Revise the following sentences so that they have a positive connotation.

   My little brother is so nosy; he always knows everyone's business.

   _____

   I can't believe how bossy Steven is!

   _____

   Jonathan lost the tournament, but maybe he can win next time, if his opponent is not so re-
   lentless.

   _____

   Now, choose a sentence from your draft. Revise it to give it a different connotation, and write it
   below.

   _____

11. Add two sentences that will strengthen the main impression you wish to create.

   _____

   _____

Editing and Proofreading

12. Cross out any misspelled homophones in the sentences below. Above each misspelling, write the
   correct word.

   I will never be able to except the idea that Jean is a better swimmer then I am. Her technique is

   so sloppy that she looks as though she swims more slowly then I do.

   Now, examine your draft. Correct any misspelled homophones on the lines below. If you have no
   misspelled homophones, write *none*.

   _____

13. Evaluate your draft according to the rubric below. List any changes that you may need to make to
   improve your speech.

	Score 4	Score 3	Score 2	Score 1
Audience and Purpose	Chooses highly effective words; clearly focuses on persuasive task	Chooses effective words; focuses on persuasive task	Occasionally uses effective words; is minimally focused on persuasive task	Poor word choice shows lack of attention to persuasive task
Organization	Uses clear, consistent organizational strategy	Uses clear organizational strategy with occasional inconsistencies	Uses inconsistent organizational strategy and illogical presentation	Lacks organizational strategy; gives confusing presentation
Elaboration	Contains specific, well-elaborated reasons that provide convincing support for the writer's position	Contains two or more moderately elaborated reasons in support of the writer's position	Contains several reasons, but few are elaborated	Contains no specific reasons
Use of Language	Contains no empty or hedging words; makes no errors in grammar, spelling, and punctuation	Contains few empty or hedging words; makes few errors in grammar, spelling, and punctuation	Contains some empty and hedging words; makes errors in grammar, spelling, and punctuation	Contains many empty or hedging words; makes many errors in grammar, spelling, and punctuation

   _____

   _____

   _____

Publishing and Presenting

14. Explain how you would revise your speech so that it could be presented as a persuasive essay.

_____
_____
_____

15. Reflect on specific techniques you discovered for persuading an audience.

_____
_____
_____
_____
_____
_____

8

Assessment for Chapter 8:
Persuasion: Advertisement
Test 1

In this test, you will be asked to create an advertisement for a new food item. Invent a dessert food, brand of pasta, or soft drink. Write your topic on the line below.

_____

Prewriting

1. Choose an imaginary brand name for the food that you want to advertise. Write your selection on the lines below.

_____

2. Circle the appropriate answers in the chart to identify your audience.

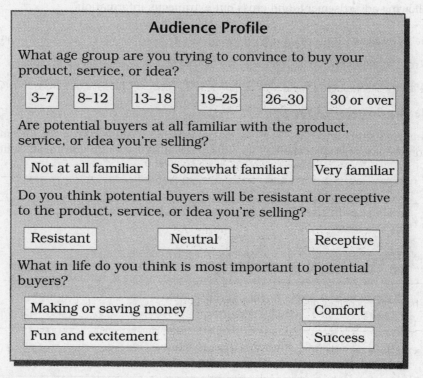

Audience Profile

What age group are you trying to convince to buy your product, service, or idea?

| 3–7 | 8–12 | 13–18 | 19–25 | 26–30 | 30 or over |

Are potential buyers at all familiar with the product, service, or idea you're selling?

| Not at all familiar | Somewhat familiar | Very familiar |

Do you think potential buyers will be resistant or receptive to the product, service, or idea you're selling?

| Resistant | Neutral | Receptive |

What in life do you think is most important to potential buyers?

| Making or saving money | Comfort |
| Fun and excitement | Success |

List two additional details that describe your audience.

_____

_____

3. Write two questions that your audience might have about your product.

_____

_____

Drafting

4. Develop your main idea by writing a slogan that uses word play or alliteration.

_____

5. Based on the product, brand, and audience that you have chosen, explain the type of statistic that would make your product more attractive to your audience. (For example, if you were creating an advertisement for chocolate chip cookies, a helpful statistic would show that many people preferred the taste of your cookie over another brand in a taste test.)

_____

_____

6. What kind of expert could you cite as a person who would recommend your product? Explain your answer.

_____

7. On a separate sheet of paper, use your notes and information from the graphic organizer to draft an advertisement.

Revising

8. Read the following advertisement, and cross out extraneous information.

> Charlie's Chocolate Chip Cookies contain the richest, melt-in-your-mouth chocolate of any choco-
> late chip cookies anywhere. Charlie only uses the highest quality ingredients for his cookies, and he
> never settles for second-best. Charlie was born in a small cabin in Chipsville, Arkansas. Buy Charlie's
> Chocolate Chip Cookies—the sweet treat.

Now, examine your draft, and cross out any extraneous information. Write the information that you eliminated on the lines below. If there is no extraneous information in your draft, write *none*.

_____

_____

9. Correct the run-on sentences below.

> Charlie's Chocolate Chip Cookies are the sweet treat try one you'll see!

_____

> Buy Charlie's Chocolate Chip Cookies they're the best

_____

> In a recent taste test, four out of five people chose Charlie's Chocolate Chip Cookies so will you.

_____

Now, examine your draft. On the line below, correct any run-on sentences. If you have no run-on sentences in your draft, write *none*.

_____

10. Circle each weak or vague adjective below, and write a replacement above it.

> Charlie's Chocolate Chip Cookies taste good.
>
> Everyone agrees that these cookies have the best chocolate chips.
>
> The cookies are moist.

Now, examine your draft. Find two weak or vague adjectives, and correct them below.

_____

_____

11. Add one sentence that will make your advertisement more persuasive.

_____

Editing and Proofreading

12. Circle the dates and ordinals below, and rewrite the correct abbreviations above them.

> Come to the grand opening of Charlie's Chocolate Chip Cookie Store, on the corner of Fiftieth
>
> Street and Tenth Avenue, on November 1, 2007!

Now, review your draft. On the lines below, correct your abbreviations of dates and ordinals. If you have no words that need to be abbreviated, write <u>none</u>.

_____

13. Evaluate your draft according to the rubric below. List any changes that you may need to make to improve your advertisement.

	Score 4	Score 3	Score 2	Score 1
Audience and Purpose	Presents effective slogan; clearly addresses persuasive task	Presents good slogan; addresses persuasive task	Presents slogan; minimally addresses persuasive task	Does not present slogan; shows lack of attention to persuasive task
Organization	Uses clear, consistent organizational strategy; clearly presents key ideas	Uses clear organizational strategy with few inconsistencies	Uses inconsistent organizational strategy; creates illogical presentation	Demonstrates lack of organizational strategy; creates confusing presentation
Elaboration	Successfully combines words and images to provide convincing, unified support for a position	Combines words and images to provide unified support for a position	Includes some words or images that detract from a position	Uses words and images that do not support a position
Use of Language	Successfully communicates an idea through clever use of language; includes very few mechanical errors	Conveys an idea through adequate use of language; includes few mechanical errors	Misuses language and lessens impact of ideas; includes many mechanical errors	Demonstrates poor use of language and confuses meaning; includes many mechanical errors

_____

_____

_____

_____

Publishing and Presenting

14. Where would you post the advertisement for your product? Explain your answer.

_____

_____

15. Were you more comfortable with the verbal or visual aspects of creating an advertisement? Explain your answer.

_____

_____

_____

Assessment for Chapter 8:
Persuasion: Advertisement
Test 2

In this test, you will be asked to write a newspaper advertisement for a product that is used in the home. Consider one of the following ideas: computers, electric drills, ceiling fans, bicycles, cordless telephones, or CD players. Write your topic on the line below.

_____

Prewriting

1. Choose an imaginary brand name for the product that you want to advertise. Write your selection on the line below, and explain why you chose this name.

_____

2. Circle the appropriate answers in the chart to identify your audience.

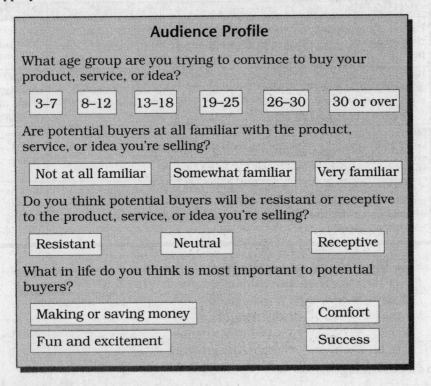

Audience Profile

What age group are you trying to convince to buy your product, service, or idea?

| 3–7 | 8–12 | 13–18 | 19–25 | 26–30 | 30 or over |

Are potential buyers at all familiar with the product, service, or idea you're selling?

| Not at all familiar | Somewhat familiar | Very familiar |

Do you think potential buyers will be resistant or receptive to the product, service, or idea you're selling?

| Resistant | Neutral | Receptive |

What in life do you think is most important to potential buyers?

| Making or saving money | Comfort |
| Fun and excitement | Success |

Write two additional details that describe your audience.

_____

_____

3. Write two questions that your audience might have about your product.

_____

_____

Drafting

4. Develop your main idea by writing a slogan that uses word play or alliteration.

_____

5. Describe the type of statistic that would make your product more attractive to your audience. (For example, if you were creating an advertisement for a vaccum cleaner, a helpful statistic would show that it cleans a rug 80% more effectively than Brand X.)

_____

_____

6. What kind of expert might recommend your product? Explain your answer.

_____

_____

7. On a separate sheet of paper, use your notes and information from the graphic organizer to draft an advertisement.

Revising

8. Read the following advertisement, and cross out extraneous information.

   Clean Scene is the most effective way to clean and polish your kitchen floor. Studies have shown that Clean Scene outcleans the leading brand by 2 to 1. Clean Scene has been on the market for two months. Buy Clean Scene—the brightest way to clean your floor. Lots of people have already bought it!

   Now, examine your draft, and cross out any extraneous information. Write one example of information you eliminated on the lines below. If your draft contains no extraneous information, write *none*.

   _____

   _____

9. Correct the run-on sentences below.

   Use Clean Scene on any no-wax floor in your house, it will safely clean and polish your wood floor. Clean Scene is specially formulated not to scratch floor surfaces.

   _____

   _____

   Now, examine your draft for run-on sentences. On the line below, write an example of one correction. If you have no run-on sentences in your draft, write *none*.

   _____

10. Circle each weak or vague adjective below, and write a replacement above it.

    Clean Scene cleans dirty floors well. It works on bad stains, and it smells nice, too.

    Now, examine your draft for weak or vague adjectives. On the lines below, write an example of one revision. If you have no weak or vague adjectives, write *none*.

    _____

    _____

11. Add one sentence that will make your advertisement more appealing.

    _____

Editing and Proofreading

12. Circle the dates and ordinals below, and rewrite the correct abbreviation above them.

> The first test trial of the product was held on March fifteenth.

> Clean Scene is ranked first in overall customer satisfaction.

> By the third use, you should see a noticeable improvement in the shine of your floor.

Now, review your draft. On the lines below, correct your abbreviations of dates and ordinals. If you have no words that need to be abbreviated, write *none*.

_____

13. Evaluate your draft according to the rubric below. List any changes that you may need to make to improve your advertisement.

	Score 4	Score 3	Score 2	Score 1
Audience and Purpose	Presents effective slogan; clearly addresses persuasive task	Presents good slogan; addresses persuasive task	Presents slogan; minimally addresses persuasive task	Does not present slogan; shows lack of attention to persuasive task
Organization	Uses clear, consistent organizational strategy; clearly presents key ideas	Uses clear organizational strategy with few inconsistencies	Uses inconsistent organizational strategy; creates illogical presentation	Demonstrates lack of organizational strategy; creates confusing presentation
Elaboration	Successfully combines words and images to provide convincing, unified support for a position	Combines words and images to provide unified support for a position	Includes some words or images that detract from a position	Uses words and images that do not support a position
Use of Language	Successfully communicates an idea through clever use of language; includes very few mechanical errors	Conveys an idea through adequate use of language; includes few mechanical errors	Misuses language and lessens impact of ideas; includes many mechanical errors	Demonstrates poor use of language and confuses meaning; includes many mechanical errors

_____

_____

_____

Publishing and Presenting

14. Where in your town might you post an advertisement for this product? Explain your answer.

_____

_____

15. Reflect on the aspect of writing an advertisement that was more comfortable for you—the verbal or the visual.

_____

_____

_____

_____

Assessment for Chapter 8: Persuasion: Advertisement
Test 3

In this test, you will be asked to write an advertisement for a special event. Consider the following ideas: a school concert or election, a charitable event, an academic contest, or an athletic competition. Write your topic on the line below.

_____

Prewriting

1. Choose an imaginary name for the event that you want to advertise. Write the name on the line below, and explain why you chose it.

   _____

2. Circle the appropriate answers in the chart to identify your audience.

   ## Audience Profile

   What age group are you trying to convince to buy your product, service, or idea?

   | 3–7 | 8–12 | 13–18 | 19–25 | 26–30 | 30 or over |

   Are potential buyers at all familiar with the product, service, or idea you're selling?

   | Not at all familiar | Somewhat familiar | Very familiar |

   Do you think potential buyers will be resistant or receptive to the product, service, or idea you're selling?

   | Resistant | Neutral | Receptive |

   What in life do you think is most important to potential buyers?

   | Making or saving money | Comfort |
   | Fun and excitement | Success |

   Write two additional details that describe your audience.

   _____

   _____

3. Write three questions that your audience might have about your topic. Explain why you think the audience would ask these questions.

   _____

   _____

   _____

   _____

Drafting

4. Develop your main idea by writing a slogan that uses word play or alliteration.

_____

5. Make sure your slogan is pithy—or full of meaning. Write an example of a pithy slogan on the line.

_____

6. What kind of facts could you use to help you advertise this event? Explain your answer.

_____

7. On a separate sheet of paper, use your notes and information from the graphic organizer to draft an advertisement.

Revising

8. Underline the key points in the advertisement below; then, number them in the order that would make the key points more prominent.

> Game time is 8:00 P.M. Come and see the high school basketball game of the century! Watch these two 15–0 teams battle it out for the state championship! Don't miss the action! Century High takes on its rival, South High at the Town Arena.

_____

_____

_____

_____

Now, locate the key points of your draft, and, on the lines below, revise one to make it more prominent.

_____

_____

9. Read the following advertisement, and cross out extraneous information.

> Watch our team rise for the prize! They have worked so hard to get to this game. South High takes on Century High in a battle for the state championship. South might win this one, because they have a better defense. Game time is 8:00 P.M. Don't miss this ultimate clash of basketball powerhouses!

Now, examine your draft, and cross out any extraneous information. Write one example of information you eliminated on the lines below. If your draft contains no extraneous information, write *none*.

_____

_____

Name _____

10. Correct the run-on sentences below.

    Cheer your team to victory at the Town Arena tip-off is at 8:00 P.M., watch the defending champ South High take on Century High for the state crown it's sure to be a fight to the finish!

    _____
    _____
    _____

Now, examine your draft. On the line below, correct any run-on sentences. If you have no run-on sentences in your draft, write *none*.

    _____

11. Add one sentence that will make your advertisement even more appealing.

    _____

Editing and Proofreading

12. Cross out the days, dates, and ordinals below, and write the correct abbreviations above them.

    The event will be held on Wednesday, January twelfth, at 721 East First Street.

Now, review your draft for correct abbreviations of dates and ordinals. Correct any errors on the line below. If you have no incorrect abbreviations of dates and ordinals, write *none*.

    _____

13. Evaluate your draft according to the rubric below. List any changes that you may need to make to improve your advertisement.

	Score 4	Score 3	Score 2	Score 1
Audience and Purpose	Presents effective slogan; clearly addresses persuasive task	Presents good slogan; addresses persuasive task	Presents slogan; minimally addresses persuasive task	Does not present slogan; shows lack of attention to persuasive task
Organization	Uses clear, consistent organizational strategy; clearly presents key ideas	Uses clear organizational strategy with few inconsistencies	Uses inconsistent organizational strategy; creates illogical presentation	Demonstrates lack of organizational strategy; creates confusing presentation
Elaboration	Successfully combines words and images to provide convincing, unified support for a position	Combines words and images to provide unified support for a position	Includes some words or images that detract from a position	Uses words and images that do not support a position
Use of Language	Successfully communicates an idea through clever use of language; includes very few mechanical errors	Conveys an idea through adequate use of language; includes few mechanical errors	Misuses language and lessens impact of ideas; includes many mechanical errors	Demonstrates poor use of language and confuses meaning; includes many mechanical errors

    _____
    _____
    _____
    _____

© Prentice-Hall, Inc.

Chapter 8: Persuasion: Advertisement • 65

Publishing and Presenting

14. Explain where your advertisement should be posted to get the best response.

_____

_____

15. Reflect on how creating your own advertisement changed, or did not change, your view of other advertisements that you see.

_____

_____

_____

Assessment for Chapter 9: Exposition: Comparison-and-Contrast Essay
Test 1

In this test, you will be asked to write a comparison-and-contrast essay of at least four paragraphs on the positive and negative aspects of two different activities, such as playing two different sports, going to school full-time versus going to work full-time; playing sports versus watching sports; or walking versus driving. Write your topic on the line below.

_____

Prewriting

1. Fill in three similarities and differences between your subjects in the chart below.

Similarities	Differences

2. Write two examples of details that you need to use to get your purpose across to your readers.

_____

3. Based on the topic, your purpose, and your audience, write two questions that will help guide your prewriting investigation about the subjects of your essay.

_____
_____
_____

Drafting

4. Create an outline for your essay, using a subject-by-subject comparison.

_____
_____
_____
_____
_____
_____

5. Based on your topic and purpose, write two examples that you could use to emphasize the similarities and differences between your subjects.

_____

_____

6. Write a fact that would support one of the statements you have made about the similarities and differences between your subjects.

_____

7. On a separate sheet of paper, use your notes and information from the graphic organizer to draft your comparison-and-contrast essay.

Revising

8. Write an appropriate topic sentence for the paragraph below.

Many studies have been conducted that show the rate of injuries for runners is sharply higher than that for walkers. There have also been numerous studies by bone specialists which indicate that runners are more prone to stress fractures as well. This increased rate of injuries for runners is the result of the increased stress on the body that running causes.

_____

Now, review your draft. Improve one of the topic sentences so that it connects more effectively to the essay topic. Write the new version below.

_____

9. Draw a vertical line to indicate where you would divide the paragraph below into two paragraphs, based on the location of the main ideas.

There are many benefits to be gained by walking. First, walking can be done by almost anyone at any age. All that is needed is a pair of supportive sneakers or shoes. One can walk anywhere—in town, through a park, or around the neighborhood. Walking can also be a social activity. One can walk alone or with a group of friends. It is an exercise that can be adapted to one's lifestyle. Walking is also a healthy alternative to running. Many studies have shown that a health regimen that includes thirty minutes of walking at least three times a week actually strengthens bones and muscles. Moreover, walking briskly burns as many calories as running.

_____

_____

Now, examine your draft. On the lines below, explain how you could divide one large paragraph into two smaller ones.

_____

_____

Name _____

10. Combine the pairs of sentences below.

> Walking is a low-impact exercise. It strengthens muscles.
>
> Walking is a flexible form of exercise. It can be adapted to suit your lifestyle.
>
> Many people prefer walking to running. They don't get injured as much when they walk.

_____

_____

Now, review your draft for two short sentences that can be combined into a single compound or complex sentence. On the lines below, write the revised sentence.

_____

_____

_____

11. Write the appropriate transitions to connect ideas in the sentences below.

> Some people claim that running is a healthier form of exercise than walking. _____, they do
>
> not cite any statistics to support this assertion. _____ they ignore any examples or studies that do
>
> not support their belief, they still cling to it.

_____

_____

Now, examine your draft. Mark a place where you can add one transition to clarify a relationship between ideas, and write the new sentence below.

_____

Editing and Proofreading

12. Insert commas in the appropriate places in the sentences below.

> While I enjoy taking walks with my friends I like to run alone. When I run I think about the events
>
> of my day. Running helps me to relax my mind my body and my spirit.

_____

_____

Review your draft for errors in comma usage. On the line below, show one example of a comma correction. If you find no comma errors, write *none*.

_____

13. Evaluate your draft according to the rubric below. List any changes that you may need to make in your essay.

	Score 4	Score 3	Score 2	Score 1
Audience and Purpose	Clearly provides a reason for a comparison-contrast analysis	Adequately provides a reason for a comparison-contrast analysis	Provides a reason for a comparison-contrast analysis	Does not provide a reason for a comparison-contrast analysis
Organization	Clearly presents information in a consistent organization best suited to the topic	Presents information using an organization suited to the topic	Chooses an organization not suited to comparison and contrast	Shows a lack of organizational strategy
Elaboration	Elaborates several ideas with facts, details, or examples; links all information to comparison and contrast	Elaborates most ideas with facts, details, or examples; links most information to comparison and contrast	Does not elaborate all ideas; does not link some details to comparison and contrast	Does not provide facts or examples to support a comparison and contrast
Use of Language	Demonstrates excellent sentence and vocabulary variety; includes very few mechanical errors	Demonstrates adequate sentence and vocabulary variety; includes few mechanical errors	Demonstrates repetitive use of sentence structure and vocabulary; includes many mechanical errors	Demonstrates poor use of language; generates confusion; includes many mechanical errors

_____
_____
_____
_____

Publishing and Presenting

14. List two places where you could publish your essay.

_____
_____

15. Reflect on what you learned about your subjects as you wrote your comparison-and-contrast essay.

_____
_____
_____

9 **Assessment for Chapter 9: Exposition: Comparison-and-Contrast Essay**
Test 2

In this test, you will be asked to write an essay of at least four paragraphs comparing and contrasting two different products or experiences. You might compare and contrast two brands of the same product, such as an electronic device, clothing, or food. You might compare and contrast experiences, such as buying a dessert versus baking it yourself, or going out to eat as opposed to preparing a meal at home. Write your topic on the line below.

_____

Prewriting

1. Fill in three similarities and differences between your subjects in the chart below.

Similarities	Differences

2. Write two examples of details that you need to use to convey your purpose to your readers.

_____

_____

3. Based on the topic, purpose, and audience, write down three questions that will help guide your prewriting investigation about the subjects of your essay.

_____

_____

_____

Drafting

4. Create an outline for your essay, using a point-by-point comparison.

_____

_____

_____

_____

_____

_____

5. Based on your topic and purpose, write two examples that you could use to emphasize the similarities and differences between your subjects.

_____

_____

6. Write a fact that would support one of the statements you have made about the similarities and differences between your subjects.

_____

_____

7. On a separate sheet of paper, use your notes and information from the graphic organizer to draft your comparison-and-contrast essay.

Revising

8. Write an appropriate topic sentence for the paragraph below.

> Washing and waxing the car yourself adds up to only a few dollars in detergent, water, and wax. Getting your car washed and waxed professionally, however, can cost more than ten dollars. Anyone can wash a car, so why would you bother taking it to a car wash? You may even save time if you wash your own car, because you can choose a convenient time to do it. There is a good chance that you will have to wait in line at the local car wash.

_____

Now, review your draft. Improve one of the topic sentences so that it connects more effectively to the essay topic. Write the new version below.

_____

9. Write a functional paragraph that could follow the paragraph above and serve as a transition to a paragraph that would discuss the benefits of having a car washed professionally.

_____

_____

Now, examine your draft, and write a functional paragraph that would serve as a transition between two ideas on the lines below. Be sure to explain where you would place this paragraph.

_____

_____

_____

10. Draw a vertical line to indicate where you would divide the paragraph below into two paragraphs, based on the location of the main ideas.

There are two good reasons for washing your own car. First, washing your own car enables you to meet your standards of cleanliness. There is no need to supervise the workers to make sure that they are following your instructions. Second, washing your own car saves money, since only the materials need to be purchased. However, washing a car by hand does have a few disadvantages. It is time-consuming, especially if you own a large car. It is also messy. The water and soap tend to get on you as much as they do on the car.

_____
_____
_____
_____

Now, review the paragraphs in your draft. Mark one or more places where you might break a paragraph into two. Choose one paragraph, and explain why it should be broken or left intact.

_____
_____

11. Combine the following pairs of sentences.

Washing your own car can be fun. It can also be time-consuming.

_____

Many people prefer to wash their own cars. Others would rather take their cars to a car wash.

_____

Car washes are more expensive. You are paying for a service.

_____

Review your draft for short sentences that can be combined into a single compound or complex sentence. On the line, write an example of one revised sentence.

_____
_____

Editing and Proofreading

12. Insert commas in the appropriate places in the sentences below.

When you are hand-washing a car it is important to have the proper detergent. Without the proper detergent you risk damaging the finish ruining the paint job and destroying the beauty of your car. Professional washers know which detergent to use so they are less likely to damage the paint.

_____
_____

Review your draft for errors in comma usage. On the line below, show one example of a comma correction. If you find no comma errors, write *none*.

_____
_____

13. Evaluate your draft according to the rubric below. List any changes that you may need to make to improve your essay.

	Score 4	Score 3	Score 2	Score 1
Audience and Purpose	Clearly provides a reason for a comparison-contrast analysis	Adequately provides a reason for a comparison-contrast analysis	Provides a reason for a comparison-contrast analysis	Does not provide a reason for a comparison-contrast analysis
Organization	Clearly presents information in a consistent organization best suited to the topic	Presents information using an organization suited to the topic	Chooses an organization not suited to comparison and contrast	Shows a lack of organizational strategy
Elaboration	Elaborates several ideas with facts, details, or examples; links all information to comparison and contrast	Elaborates most ideas with facts, details, or examples; links most information to comparison and contrast	Does not elaborate all ideas; does not link some details to comparison and contrast	Does not provide facts or examples to support a comparison and contrast
Use of Language	Demonstrates excellent sentence and vocabulary variety; includes very few mechanical errors	Demonstrates adequate sentence and vocabulary variety; includes few mechanical errors	Demonstrates repetitive use of sentence structure and vocabulary; includes many mechanical errors	Demonstrates poor use of language; generates confusion; includes many mechanical errors

_____

_____

_____

Publishing and Presenting

14. If you were to publish your essay in a school paper, do you think your audience would agree or disagree with your conclusions? Explain your answer.

_____

_____

15. Reflect on the advice you might give to a student who is preparing to write a comparison-and-contrast essay.

_____

_____

Assessment for Chapter 9: Exposition: Comparison-and-Contrast Essay
Test 3

In this test, you will be asked to write a three-to-four paragraph essay comparing and contrasting two forms of entertainment. You might consider one of the following ideas to help you decide on a topic for your essay: classical music and jazz, poetry and rap music, video games and outdoor sports. Write your topic on the line below.

_____

Prewriting

1. Fill in three similarities and differences between your subjects in the chart below.

Similarities	Differences

2. Write two examples of details that you might use to get your purpose across to your readers.

_____

_____

3. Based on the topic, purpose, and audience, write down four questions that will help guide your prewriting investigation about the subjects of your essay.

_____

_____

_____

_____

Drafting

4. Outline your comparison-and-contrast essay on the lines below, using either point-by-point or subject-by-subject comparison.

_____

_____

_____

_____

_____

Explain why you chose this method to organize your essay.

_____

_____

5. Based on your topic and purpose, write three examples that you could use to emphasize the similarities and differences between your subjects.

_____

_____

_____

6. State a fact that would support one of the statements you have made about the similarities and differences between your subjects.

_____

_____

7. On a separate sheet of paper, use your notes and information from the graphic organizer to draft your comparison-and-contrast essay.

Revising

8. Read the topic sentence below, and write three sentences that would support it in a paragraph.

   Both outdoor sports and video games improve eye-hand coordination.

_____

_____

_____

_____

_____

Now, review your draft, and find a topic sentence in one of your paragraphs. Improve two of your sentences so that they support the topic sentence more strongly. Write the new sentences below.

_____

_____

9. Write a functional paragraph that will follow the topical paragraph below and will serve as a transition to a paragraph that examines the ways in which classical music is similar to jazz.

Classical music is performed according to certain "rules." These rules are written into the composition and instruct the musician whether to play the music quickly or slowly, softly or loudly, or in a march or waltz tempo. The Italian words that are used to describe these features of the music are learned by musicians from their earliest lessons, and are commonly understood by all of them.

_____

_____

Now, examine your draft and write a functional paragraph that would serve as a transition between two ideas. Mark the place in your draft where you would place this paragraph.

_____

_____

_____

10. Use transitions to combine the pairs of sentences below.

Poetry may deal with real-world social or political issues. Folk music may deal with these issues, too.

You take a job to earn money. You choose a career to gain satisfaction.

_____

_____

_____

_____

Now, review your draft for short sentences that might be combined into a single compound or complex sentence. Write the revised sentence on the lines below.

_____

_____

11. Write the appropriate transitions to connect ideas in the sentences below.

Classical music employs brass and woodwind instruments. _____, jazz uses them to create its special sound. Classical music, _____, may employ a number of ancient instruments, such as a harpsichord. Jazz, _____, employs a smaller variety of instruments with more varied effects.

_____

_____

Now, examine your draft. Mark a place where you can add a transition to clarify a relationship between ideas. Write the new sentence below.

_____

_____

Editing and Proofreading

12. Insert or delete commas as necessary in the sentences below.

> Jazz developed in the 1920's, in Harlem, New York. It quickly gained popularity and soon people
>
> from all over the country were flocking to Harlem to listen, to jazz. Eighty years later you can still
>
> visit Harlem and listen to jazz in many small clubs.

_____

_____

Review your draft for errors in comma usage. On the line below, show one example of a comma correction. If you find no comma errors, write *none*.

_____

13. Evaluate your draft according to the rubric below. List any changes that you may need to make to improve your essay

	Score 4	Score 3	Score 2	Score 1
Audience and Purpose	Clearly provides a reason for a comparison-contrast analysis	Adequately provides a reason for a comparison-contrast analysis	Provides a reason for a comparison-contrast analysis	Does not provide a reason for a comparison-contrast analysis
Organization	Clearly presents information in a consistent organization best suited to the topic	Presents information using an organization suited to the topic	Chooses an organization not suited to comparison and contrast	Shows a lack of organizational strategy
Elaboration	Elaborates several ideas with facts, details, or examples; links all information to comparison and contrast	Elaborates most ideas with facts, details, or examples; links most information to comparison and contrast	Does not elaborate all ideas; does not link some details to comparison and contrast	Does not provide facts or examples to support a comparison and contrast
Use of Language	Demonstrates excellent sentence and vocabulary variety; includes very few mechanical errors	Demonstrates adequate sentence and vocabulary variety; includes few mechanical errors	Demonstrates repetitive use of sentence structure and vocabulary; includes many mechanical errors	Demonstrates poor use of language; generates confusion; includes many mechanical errors

_____

_____

_____

_____

Publishing and Presenting

14. Describe the elements you would use if you were to give a multimedia presentation of your essay.

_____

_____

15. What did you learn about your essay subjects as you gathered details?

_____

_____

Assessment for Chapter 10:
Exposition: Cause-and-Effect Essay
Test 1

In this test, you will be asked to write a cause-and-effect essay of at least three paragraphs on a school-related issue. You might consider the effects of computers on education, the effects of lengthening the school day on students and teachers, or the effects of part-time work on students. Write your topic on the line below.

_____

Prewriting

1. Narrow your topic by creating a web. Write your topic in the center circle, and write connected subtopics in the circles around it. Write the subtopic you selected on the line below.

_____

2. Describe your audience and purpose for writing on the lines below.

   My audience is _____.

   My purpose is _____.

3. Based on the information you have gathered above, write two examples of concrete, specific details that you will use to engage your audience and accomplish your purpose.

   _____

   _____

   _____

Drafting

4. Organize your ideas according to their order of importance. Start your list with the least important idea and conclude with the most important idea.

   _____

   _____

   _____

   _____

   _____

   _____

5. Give an example that will help readers connect your topic with their experiences.

   _____

6. Share an insight about your topic to give your writing a more personal touch.

   _____

7. On a separate sheet of paper, use your notes and information from the graphic organizer to draft your essay.

Revising

8. Check the organization of your essay by creating an outline on the lines below. Make a numbered list of each paragraph in the essay, and beside each number, write a few words summarizing the idea of the paragraph. If you need to reorganize the order of the paragraphs, write the new order.

   Order of Importance

   1. _____

   2. _____

   3. _____

   4. _____

9. Cross out each conjunction that is used incorrectly in the sentences below. Write the correct conjunction above it.

   The use of computers in schools has enabled students to learn programs that they will use when they enter the world of work; however, it has given them access to information on the Internet. Computers have made the work of teachers easier; otherwise, they are able to devise creative lessons that incorporate the use of computers. There are some difficulties associated with the use of computers, and they are relatively minor compared to the benefits.

   Now, review your draft. Correct any errors in the use of conjunctions on the line below. If you do not have any errors, write *none*.

   _____

10. Create complete sentences for each subordinate clause listed below.

    before computers were introduced in schools

    _____

    that many students have learned to use computers as research tools

    _____

    which are the tools of the twenty-first century

    _____

    Now, examine your draft. Find a subordinate clause that should be part of a complete sentence, and correct it below. If your essay does not contain any stray subordinate clauses, write *none*.

    _____

11. Cross out any unnecessary qualifiers in the sentences below.

    It seems that computers have eased the stress of completing homework for teachers and students. Computerized grading programs have tended to save teachers time in determining students' grades. Students can also use computers to complete their research rather more quickly.

    Now, examine your draft. Write down one unnecessary qualifier below. If you don't find any, write *none*.

    _____

Editing and Proofreading

12. Rewrite the sentences below so that they contain nonessential expressions.

    The word processing programs in school are easy to use.

    Students can use the library to do research on the computer.

    The Internet is an easy-to-use source for information.

    _____

    _____

    _____

    Now, examine your draft. Choose one sentence, and rewrite it so that it contains one nonessential expression.

    _____

13. Evaluate your draft according to the rubric below. List any changes that you may need to make to improve your essay.

	Score 4	Score 3	Score 2	Score 1
Audience and Purpose	Consistently targets an audience; clearly identifies purpose in thesis statement	Targets an audience; identifies purpose in thesis statement	Misses a target audience by including a wide range of word choice and details; presents no clear purpose	Addresses no specific audience or purpose
Organization	Presents a clear, consistent organizational strategy to show cause and effect	Presents a clear organizational strategy with occasional inconsistencies; shows cause and effect	Presents an inconsistent organizational strategy; creates illogical presentation of causes and effects	Demonstrates a lack of organizational strategy; creates a confusing presentation
Elaboration	Successfully links causes with effects; fully elaborates connections among ideas	Links causes with effects; elaborates connections among most ideas	Links some causes with some effects; elaborates connections among some ideas	Develops and elaborates no links between causes and effects
Use of Language	Uses words precisely; presents very few mechanical errors	Uses words precisely; presents few mechanical errors	Contains some imprecise words; presents many mechanical errors	Demonstrates poor use of words; presents many mechanical errors

_____

_____

_____

_____

Publishing and Presenting

14. Describe a group of students who might be interested in reading your essay.

_____

_____

15. What new information about your topic did you discover, as you wrote this essay?

_____

_____

_____

Assessment for Chapter 10: Exposition: Cause-and-Effect Essay
Test 2

In this test, you will be asked to write a cause-and-effect essay of at least three paragraphs on issues that people face every day. You might consider the effects of a college education on a career choice, the effects of taking up a hobby, or the effects of traveling on your view of the world. Write your topic on the line below.

_____

Prewriting

1. Narrow your topic by creating a web. Write your topic in the center circle, and write connected subtopics in the circles around it. Write the subtopic you selected on the line below.

_____

_____

2. Describe your audience and purpose for writing on the lines below.

   My audience is _____.

   My purpose is _____.

3. Based on the information you have gathered above, write two examples of concrete, specific details that you will use to engage your audience and accomplish your purpose.

   _____

   _____

   _____

Drafting

4. Organize the parts of your essay, according to their order of importance.

   _____
   _____
   _____
   _____
   _____
   _____

5. Give an example that will help readers connect your topic with their experiences.

   _____
   _____

6. Share an insight about your topic that will convey your attitude toward your subject.

   _____
   _____

7. On a separate sheet of paper, use your notes and information from the graphic organizer to draft your essay.

Revising

8. Rewrite the two middle sentences in the paragraph below so that they flow with the ideas of the topic sentence and last sentence of the paragraph.

   Learning a marketable skill will make it easier to get a job. My brother trained to become a me-
   chanic. Many people who don't learn a trade end up in dead-end jobs with no prospect of advance-
   ment. Learning a trade enables a person to gain a responsible position in society and to earn a
   decent income.

   _____
   _____
   _____
   _____

   Now, reread your draft. Improve the flow of one paragraph, and write the new version below.

   _____
   _____
   _____
   _____
   _____

9. Connect the ideas in the sentences below using three proper conjunctions in the spaces below.

Someone who is at a trade school or who is in training with a company has a good chance of securing employment. He or she will be more educated. _____ There is a better chance of getting and keeping a job. _____ Specific workplace skills such as plumbing or computer repair are in high demand. _____ Anyone who specializes in these areas has a good chance of securing a well-paying job.

_____

_____

_____

Now, examine your draft. Correct any errors in conjunction use on the lines below. If your essay has no errors in the use of conjunctions, write *none*.

_____

10. Add a subordinate clause to each independent clause below.

Many unskilled workers have difficulty finding jobs.

Computer technology is a growing field.

Vocational training can lead to a high-paying job.

_____

_____

Now, review your draft. Choose two simple sentences, and expand them by adding subordinate clauses.

_____

_____

_____

11. Cross out any unnecessary qualifiers in the sentences below.

Unemployment rates are sort of higher for those people who do not have vocational skills. Therefore, it is rather important to take advantage of vocational training opportunities that are offered in high school. If you have such training when you enter the work force, you will be kind of ready for work.

Now, examine your draft. Write down two unnecessary qualifiers below. If you have no unnecessary qualifiers, write *none*.

_____

Editing and Proofreading

12. Rewrite each sentence, converting the essential expressions to nonessential expressions.

Paul has decided to attend Teterboro State the aviation school.

Secretary of Labor Alexis Herman has announced a new government initiative aimed at funding vocational training programs.

Now, examine your draft. Choose two sentences and convert them so that they have nonessential expressions. Write your revised sentences on the lines below.

_____

_____

_____

13. Evaluate your draft according to the rubric below. List any changes that you may need to make to improve your essay.

	Score 4	Score 3	Score 2	Score 1
Audience and Purpose	Consistently targets an audience; clearly identifies purpose in thesis statement	Targets an audience; identifies purpose in thesis statement	Misses a target audience by including a wide range of word choice and details; presents no clear purpose	Addresses no specific audience or purpose
Organization	Presents a clear, consistent organizational strategy to show cause and effect	Presents a clear organizational strategy with occasional inconsistencies; shows cause and effect	Presents an inconsistent organizational strategy; creates illogical presentation of causes and effects	Demonstrates a lack of organizational strategy; creates a confusing presentation
Elaboration	Successfully links causes with effects; fully elaborates connections among ideas	Links causes with effects; elaborates connections among most ideas	Links some causes with some effects; elaborates connections among some ideas	Develops and elaborates no links between causes and effects
Use of Language	Uses words precisely; presents very few mechanical errors	Uses words precisely; presents few mechanical errors	Contains some imprecise words; presents many mechanical errors	Demonstrates poor use of words; presents many mechanical errors

_____

_____

_____

_____

_____

Publishing and Presenting

14. Describe the kind of discussion you might expect to have if you were to share your essay with your peers.

_____

_____

15. Reflect on one piece of advice you would give to a friend who is writing a cause-and-effect essay.

_____

_____

Assessment for Chapter 10: Exposition: Cause-and-Effect Essay
Test 3

In this test, you will be asked to write a three- to four-paragraph essay about the effect of an idea or invention on our future lifestyles. You might consider the effect of e-mail on communication, the effect of high-speed trains on transportation, or the effect of a gasoline shortage. Write your topic on the line below.

_____

Prewriting

1. Narrow your topic by creating a web. Write your topic in the center circle, and write connected subtopics in the circles around it. Write the subtopic you selected on the line below.

_____

_____

2. Describe your audience and purpose for writing on the lines below.

   Audience: _____

   Purpose: _____

3. Based on the information you have gathered above, write three examples of details that you will use to show how one action or situation led to another.

   _____

   _____

   _____

Drafting

4. Select the order in which you will organize your ideas, and use that order to create an outline for your essay. Explain why you selected this order to organize your information.

_____

_____

_____

_____

_____

_____

5. Give an example that will help readers connect to your information.

_____

6. Share an insight about your topic that will convey your tone.

_____

7. On a separate sheet of paper, use your notes and information from the graphic organizer to draft your essay.

Revising

8. Check the order of your paragraphs by making a new outline of your draft.

_____

_____

_____

_____

If you need to rearrange the order of the paragraphs, explain why on the lines below.

_____

_____

9. Rewrite each pair of sentences as one sentence, using correlative or subordinate conjunctions.

Space travel will be possible in the future. It will be expensive.

There have been many advances in space technology. These advances can be used to refine space

travel.

Today, it takes approximately four years for a spaceship to reach Mars. In fifty years, that travel

time may be cut in half.

_____

_____

Now, review your draft. Add variety to the sentence structure by combining two or three sentences using conjunctions. Write the revisions below.

_____

_____

_____

10. Write a topic sentence and a concluding sentence that flow with the ideas presented in the sentences below.

         Already, many people "telecommute" to work through the use of the Internet and e-mail. This technology enables workers to access information and communicate with their colleagues without leaving home.

Topic Sentence: _____

Concluding Sentence: _____

_____

_____

_____

Now, review your draft. Find the parts of any paragraphs that do not contribute to the main idea, and write them below. If you have no errors in paragraph flow, write *none*.

_____

11. Add a subordinate clause to each independent clause below.

         New technology will radically change everyday life.

_____

         Some people will be at a serious disadvantage.

_____

         Computers will become even more integral to daily life activities.

_____

Now, explain how each subordinate clause elaborates on the idea in the independent clause.

_____

_____

Now, review your draft. Add subordinate clauses to elaborate on the ideas presented in two simple sentences. Write the revised sentences on the lines below.

_____

_____

Editing and Proofreading

12. Add commas to set off any nonessential expressions in the sentences below.

         Technology which has developed rapidly over the past decade intimidates many people.

         One of the areas that has changed most rapidly during this time period is Internet access which has increased tremendously in recent years.

         "Surfing the net" as it is popularly called refers to the act of looking for and finding information on the Internet.

Now, examine your essay. Add or delete commas where appropriate. Write two corrected sentences on the lines below. If your essay does not contain errors in comma usage, write *none*.

_____

_____

13. Evaluate your draft according to the rubric below. Write any changes that you may need to make to improve your essay.

	Score 4	Score 3	Score 2	Score 1
Audience and Purpose	Consistently targets an audience; clearly identifies purpose in thesis statement	Targets an audience; identifies purpose in thesis statement	Misses a target audience by including a wide range of word choice and details; presents no clear purpose	Addresses no specific audience or purpose
Organization	Presents a clear, consistent organizational strategy to show cause and effect	Presents a clear organizational strategy with occasional inconsistencies; shows cause and effect	Presents an inconsistent organizational strategy; creates illogical presentation of causes and effects	Demonstrates a lack of organizational strategy; creates a confusing presentation
Elaboration	Successfully links causes with effects; fully elaborates connections among ideas	Links causes with effects; elaborates connections among most ideas	Links some causes with some effects; elaborates connections among some ideas	Develops and elaborates no links between causes and effects
Use of Language	Uses words precisely; presents very few mechanical errors	Uses words precisely; presents few mechanical errors	Contains some imprecise words; presents many mechanical errors	Demonstrates poor use of words; presents many mechanical errors

_____

_____

_____

Publishing and Presenting

14. List two publications where you can publish your essay, either in your school or your community. Explain why your essay might be of interest to their readers.

_____

_____

_____

15. Imagine that a friend of yours is writing a cause-and-effect essay. Give her three pieces of helpful advice.

_____

_____

_____

_____

Assessment for Chapter 11:
Exposition: Problem-and-Solution Essay
Test 1

In this test, you will be asked to write a problem-and-solution essay of at least three paragraphs. You might consider these problems: a gap in communication between teachers and students, a difference of opinion between local store owners and teenagers, or a conflict between two of your friends. Write your topic on the line below.

_____

Prewriting

1. Create a web to help you narrow your topic. Write your broad topic in the center circle. Then, write more specific topics in the connected circles.

Write the narrowed topic on which you will base your essay on the line below.

_____

_____

2. Narrow your purpose for writing by explaining how the specific topic presents a problem.

_____

_____

_____

3. Complete the T-chart below by listing at least one aspect of the problem and two possible solutions.

Problem	Solution

Drafting

4. Use chronological order to organize your essay.
   Clear statement of the problem:

   _____

   _____

   Order of steps for solution:

   _____

   _____

   _____

   _____

5. Elaborate on how a historical or personal example can support your idea.

   _____

   _____

6. On the line below, write a quotation or a statistic that supports your recommended solution.

   _____

7. On a separate sheet of paper, use your notes and information from the graphic organizers to draft your essay.

Revising

8. Write an appropriate topic sentence for the paragraph below.

   First, you need to develop a plan of attack. Make a list of qualities that you want in the college of your dreams. Next, begin your research for a college that fits your requirements. You may look in publications that list information about colleges, examine the Web sites of schools in which you are interested, or talk to your guidance counselor about the type of college that you are looking for.

   _____

   Now, review your draft. Improve one of your topic sentences so that it connects more effectively to the essay topic. Write the new version below.

   _____

Name _____

9. Rewrite the two sentences below into three or four shorter sentences.

> Changing the oil in a car is a fairly straightforward procedure, as long as you follow all of the steps involved. Nevertheless, there will always be someone who doesn't follow these steps carefully, and the results are sometimes disastrous.

_____

_____

_____

_____

Now, review your draft. Choose a long sentence, and rewrite it as two shorter sentences on the lines below.

_____

_____

10. Rewrite the topic sentences below so that they contain subject complements.

> Talking to your parents will solve the problem.
> You need to follow directions when baking a soufflé.
> Try to eliminate any outside issues when discussing your request.

_____

_____

_____

Now, review your draft. Choose one topic sentence, and rewrite it so that it contains a subject complement.

_____

11. Cross out the words that create redundancies in the following sentences.

> Remember that the baking process first begins when the dish is placed in a heated oven.

> If you are puzzled over a problem, you need to speak aloud to get assistance.

> Make sure that the cake is surrounded on all sides with the icing.

_____

_____

Now, review your draft. On the lines below, list any redundant words that you find. If your essay does not contain any redundancies, write *none*.

_____

_____

Editing and Proofreading

12. Insert hyphens or dashes in each of the following sentences.

> The greenish blue tint of the fabric matched her eyes.

> The ex football player is now a sports broadcaster.

> My brother's graduation which was held outdoors was a beautiful ceremony.

Now, examine your draft. Insert hyphens or dashes as needed, and write your corrections on the line below. If you do not need to insert any hyphens or dashes in your essay, write *none*.

_____

13. Evaluate your draft according to the rubric below. Write any changes that you may need to make to improve your essay.

	Score 4	Score 3	Score 2	Score 1
Audience and Purpose	Contains language and details to engage audience and accomplish purpose	Contains language and details appropriate for audience and that help contribute to overall effect	Contains some language and details not suited for audience; contains some details that detract from purpose	Contains language and details that are not geared for a particular audience; has an unclear purpose
Organization	Is organized consistently, logically, and effectively	Has consistent organization	Has inconsistent organization	Is disorganized and confusing
Elaboration	Has a solution that is clearly laid out, along with details that support or explain it	Has a solution that is supported with details	Has a stated solution, but it contains few details to support it	Has unclear solution, and no details are given to support it
Use of Language	Contains precise words and no redundancies; contains no errors in grammar, punctuation, or spelling	Contains effective words and few redundancies; contains few errors in grammar, punctuation, and spelling	Contains few precise words and some redundancies; contains some errors in grammar, punctuation, and spelling	Contains imprecise words and many redundancies; contains many errors in grammar, punctuation, and spelling

_____

_____

_____

_____

Publishing and Presenting

14. List two places where it would be useful to publish this essay.

_____

_____

15. Name one thing you learned about writing as you revised your essay.

_____

_____

Assessment for Chapter 11: Exposition: Problem-and-Solution Essay
Test 2

In this test, you will be asked to write a problem-and-solution essay of at least three paragraphs. You might consider one of the following issues: dealing with being a newcomer to your school, dealing with sibling rivalry, or dealing with adults' expectations. Write your topic on the line below.

_____

Prewriting

1. Create a web to help you narrow your topic. Write your broad topic in the center circle. Then, write more specific topics in the connected circles.

Write the narrowed topic on which you will base your essay on the line below.

_____

2. Narrow your purpose for writing by explaining how the specific topic presents a problem.

_____

_____

_____

3. Complete the T-chart below by listing at least one aspect of the problem and two possible solutions.

Problem	Solution

Drafting

4. Use chronological order to organize your essay.
   Clear statement of the problem:

   _____

   _____

   Order of steps for solution:

   _____

   _____

   _____

   _____

5. Elaborate on how a historical or personal example can support your idea.

   _____

   _____

6. On the line below, write a quotation or a statistic that supports your recommended solution.

   _____

7. On a separate sheet of paper, use your notes and information from the graphic organizer to draft your essay.

Revising

8. Write an appropriate topic sentence for the paragraph below.

   If possible, visit a class and note how the professor and students interact with each other. Talk to the students about their workloads and the quality of work that is demanded of them. These observations and informal interviews will provide you with insights into the academic life at colleges that statistics in guidebooks won't give you.

   _____

   Now, review your draft. Improve one of your topic sentences so that it connects more effectively to the essay topic. Write the new version below.

   _____

9. Explain how you would vary the organization of the paragraph on the previous page so that the topic sentence could be placed at the end of the paragraph.

_____

_____

10. Rewrite the topic sentences below so that they contain subject complements.

Parents must talk to their children before they set a curfew.

_____

Students should designate a quiet place in their homes as a place to study.

_____

Eating a balanced diet of foods will lead to better health.

_____

Now, review your draft. Choose one topic sentence, and rewrite it so that it contains a subject complement.

_____

_____

11. Cross out the words that create redundancies in the following sentences.

Of course, when you feel the tension first begin to rise, you must use a calming technique to prevent any further hostility.

There are various different ways to remain calm in a tense situation.

It is important not to speak to an unknown stranger when you are in an unfamiliar place.

Now, review your draft. On the lines below, list any redundant words that you find. If your essay does not contain any redundancies, write *none*.

_____

_____

Editing and Proofreading

12. Insert a hyphen or dash in each of the following sentences.

Send a self addressed, stamped envelope with your application.

The picnic was an all day affiar.

I think I left my hat in the kitchen no, it's over here.

Now, examine your draft. Insert hyphens or dashes as needed, and write your corrections on the line below. If you do not need to insert any hyphens or dashes in your essay, write *none*.

_____

_____

13. Evaluate your draft according to the rubric below. Write any changes that you may need to make to improve your essay.

	Score 4	Score 3	Score 2	Score 1
Audience and Purpose	Contains language and details to engage audience and accomplish purpose	Contains language and details appropriate for audience and that help contribute to overall effect	Contains some language and details not suited for audience; contains some details that detract from purpose	Contains language and details that are not geared for a particular audience; has an unclear purpose
Organization	Is organized consistently, logically, and effectively	Has consistent organization	Has inconsistent organization	Is disorganized and confusing
Elaboration	Has a solution that is clearly laid out, along with details that support or explain it	Has a solution that is supported with details	Has a stated solution, but it contains few details to support it	Has unclear solution, and no details are given to support it
Use of Language	Contains precise words and no redundancies; contains no errors in grammar, punctuation, or spelling	Contains effective words and few redundancies; contains few errors in grammar, punctuation, and spelling	Contains few precise words and some redundancies; contains some errors in grammar, punctuation, and spelling	Contains imprecise words and many redundancies; contains many errors in grammar, punctuation, and spelling

_____

_____

_____

_____

Publishing and Presenting

14. Explain how you would publish this essay to ensure that your peers would read it.

_____

_____

15. Reflect on how using a web helped you to narrow your topic.

_____

_____

Assessment for Chapter 11: Exposition: Problem-and-Solution Essay
Test 3

In this test, you will be asked to write a problem-and-solution essay of about three or four paragraphs in which you examine an issue that affects your community. You might consider an obstacle faced by a group of people in your community, such as senior citizens, teenagers, or preschool-aged children. Write your topic on the line below.

_____

Prewriting

1. Create a web to help you narrow your topic. Write your broad topic in the center circle. Then, write more specific topics in the connected circles.

Write the narrowed topic on which you will base your essay on the line below.

_____

2. Identify your audience, and explain why this audience is an appropriate one for your essay.

_____

Write three details or explanations that you will have to include to meet your audience's needs.

_____

_____

_____

3. Complete the T-chart below by listing at least one aspect of the problem and two possible solutions.

Problem	Solution

Drafting

4. List and organize the parts of your essay, using either chronological order or order of importance as a basis for your organization. Explain why you chose to organize your essay in the way that you did.

_____

_____

_____

_____

_____

_____

_____

5. Use one of the five points of illumination—comparative evidence, historical example, personal example, statistics, or quotations—to support your solution.

_____

_____

_____

6. Explain why you chose the particular point of illumination above to elaborate on your topic.

_____

_____

7. On a separate sheet of paper, use your notes and information from the graphic organizers to draft your essay.

Name _____

Revising

8. Read the paragraph below. Underline the section in which the balance of ideas needs to be improved, and explain how you would improve it.

> One major problem related to traffic congestion is the air pollution it generates. Too many people commute alone in their cars, and as a result there are too many cars belching their exhaust fumes into the air. These exhaust fumes contain carbon dioxide and carbon monoxide gases, which are harmful to humans. What should we do about it? Perhaps we need to find a way to encourage people to carpool so that there will be fewer cars—and, as a result—fewer ways in which these dangerous gases are released into the air.

_____

_____

Now, examine your draft. Explain which areas need to be revised for better balance. If your essay does not require this type of revision, write *none*.

_____

9. Write a topic sentence for the paragraph below, and explain where you would place it so that it adds impact to the paragraph.

> When more people ride in one car, there will be fewer cars on the road. Thus, there will be not only less traffic congestion, but also less air pollution. Other alternatives to driving to work alone include walking or taking public transportation. Whatever option people select, the result will be the same: Traffic congestion and air pollution will be reduced.

Topic sentence: _____

Location: _____

Now, review your draft. Identify the topic sentences that should be rearranged, and explain your answer on the lines below. If your essay does not require this type of revision, write *none*.

_____

_____

_____

10. Rewrite the topic sentences below so that they contain subject complements.

   Walking to work saves energy and money.

   _____

   Walking also strengthens muscles.

   _____

   Commuting to work, on the other hand, creates stress.

   _____

   Now, review your draft. Choose one topic sentence, and rewrite it so that it contains a subject complement.

   _____

11. Cross out the words that create redundancies in the following sentences.

   Call now to receive your free gift!

   Sunlight was reflected back from the pond and into my eyes.

   An unknown stranger suddenly appeared at the door.

   Now, review your draft. On the line below, list any redundant words that you find. If your essay does not contain any redundancies, write *none*.

   _____

Editing and Proofreading

12. Insert hyphens or dashes in each of the following sentences.

   My mother, an ex army officer, is now an English teacher at the high school.

   An all day ceremony was recently held at the army base where my mother was stationed.

   The well attended ceremony was can you believe it? even broadcast on the evening news.

   Now, examine your draft. Insert hyphens or dashes as needed, and write your corrections on the line below. If you do not need to insert any hyphens or dashes in your essay, write *none*.

   _____

13. Evaluate your draft according to the rubric below. List any changes that you may need to make to improve your essay.

	Score 4	Score 3	Score 2	Score 1
Audience and Purpose	Contains language and details to engage audience and accomplish purpose	Contains language and details appropriate for audience and that help contribute to overall effect	Contains some language and details not suited for audience; contains some details that detract from purpose	Contains language and details that are not geared for a particular audience; has an unclear purpose
Organization	Is organized consistently, logically, and effectively	Has consistent organization	Has inconsistent organization	Is disorganized and confusing
Elaboration	Has a solution that is clearly laid out, along with details that support or explain it	Has a solution that is supported with details	Has a stated solution, but it contains few details to support it	Has unclear solution, and no details are given to support it
Use of Language	Contains precise words and no redundancies; contains no errors in grammar, punctuation, or spelling	Contains effective words and few redundancies; contains few errors in grammar, punctuation, and spelling	Contains few precise words and some redundancies; contains some errors in grammar, punctuation, and spelling	Contains imprecise words and many redundancies; contains many errors in grammar, punctuation, and spelling

_____

_____

_____

_____

Publishing and Presenting

14. Explain why you might want to publish your essay in at least one community publication.

_____

_____

_____

_____

15. Reflect on a writing strategy that you tried while you were writing this essay. Was it successful? Why or why not?

_____

_____

_____

_____

_____

Assessment for Chapter 12:
Research: Documented Essay
Test 1

In this test, you'll use the work of Sarah, a student like you, who is writing a documented essay on endangered species.

Prewriting

Sarah used a variety of sources for her documented essay. Here are some note cards she made:

Note card 1

<u>Definition of endangered species</u>: a species of plant or animal that is in immediate danger of extinction throughout all or part of its range. A species may also be classified as threatened if it is likely to become endangered in the near future.

<u>Importance of extinction</u>: Less than 1 percent of all species that have ever lived exist today. Extinction may occur at a constant rate or abruptly, such as the extinction of the dinosaurs. Normal extinction rates are called "background rates," but extinction rates beyond the background rate are what we are concerned about when we talk about endangered species.

<u>McGraw-Hill Multimedia Encyclopedia of Science and Technology</u>

Note card 2

Example of endangered species: Tiger
Trading in tigers became illegal in 1975—Convention on International Trade of Endangered Species.
Illegal markets for tigers still exist openly in Cambodia, Indonesia, Laos, Myanmar, Vietnam.
Use of tiger parts such as bones in traditional Asian medicine—this practice is a threat to tigers.
Also a large worldwide market for tiger skins—used as rugs, clothing accessories, good luck charms
Estimated—only 5000–7500 tigers remain in the wild.
<u>Environmental News Network</u>, 3/31/00, http://enn.com/news/enn-stories/2000/03/03312000/tigerrep_11547.asp

Note card 3

Efforts to save tigers: Siberian Tiger Project. Siberian and American scientists worked side by side to develop a research plan, used in Russia.
First established in 1989: Scientists helped communities develop cottage industries that would replace the hunting of tigers for revenue.
These programs have become so successful that other communities are asking to become part of the new economy.

<u>Seattle Times</u>, 3/28/00

Note card 4

"Sumatran tiger in Indonesia is being hunted to extinction. Between 1998–2000, 66 tigers were poached, with 24 taken from a national park."
Suspected that poaching of tigers has been running at this level for 6 years.
Whole tiger pelts can sell for between $1250 and $7300.
Egyptian authorities also announced that they seized 304 lb of smuggled elephant tusks, valued at $300,000.

<u>The New York Times</u>, 3/30/00

1. Based on the information that she has gathered on these note cards, show how Sarah could narrow her topic by looping for three minutes on the lines below.

_____

_____

_____

_____

_____

2. What should be Sarah's purpose for writing? Write two details that would help accomplish Sarah's purpose for writing this essay.

_____

_____

_____

3. List the types of sources that Sarah has used so far to conduct her research.

   _____

   _____

   Give an example of another source that might be helpful to Sarah.

   _____

Drafting

4. Based on the information that she has gathered so far in the research process, outline Sarah's essay:

   Introduction: Main Idea: _____

   Body: 1. _____

         2. _____

         3. _____

   Conclusion: _____

5. Which note card would Sarah use to support her main idea? Explain your answer.

   _____

   _____

6. Give an example of a detail on one of Sarah's note cards that will need more elaboration in her draft. Explain your answer.

   _____

   _____

Revising

Use Sarah's introductory paragraph to answer questions 7–9 below.

> A species or plant is endangered if it is in immediate danger of extinction throughout all or part of its range. While extinction is part of the process of nature, and in fact less than one percent of all species are still alive today, there is cause for concern when extinction rates go far beyond the normal rate found in nature. For example, elephants are in danger of extinction. Even though there are efforts underway to save their dwindling populations, tigers are currently being hunted to the point of extinction in many countries, and that's why I'm writing about the tiger.

7. Write two details that could be eliminated to improve the unity of the paragraph.

   _____

   _____

8. Underline the topic sentence in the paragraph. Is it in the appropriate place, or should it be moved? Explain your answer.

   _____

   _____

   _____

9. Circle a word that is repeated several times in the paragraph. Rewrite one of the sentences, using a synonym for the repeated word.

   _____

10. Rewrite the following sentences so that the pronouns agree with their antecedents.

    Both tigers and elephants are endangered species. It have been hunted for the medicinal and fi-

    nancial benefit their carcasses offer. Many scientists have tried to prevent this situation, but his ef-

    forts have been only partially successful.

    _____

    _____

11. What tone should Sarah adopt in her essay? Write three words that Sarah might include in her essay
    in order to convey this tone.

    _____

    _____

Editing and Proofreading

12. Give an example of a detail from one of Sarah's note cards that should be cited as a direct quotation
    in her essay. Explain why.

    _____

    _____

13. Give an example of a detail from one of Sarah's note cards that could be used as an indirect
    quotation.

    _____

    Paraphrase the detail above.

    _____

Publishing and Presenting

14. Describe one visual aid that Sarah might use while presenting her essay to the class.

    _____

15. Reflect on one thing you learned about doing research for a documented essay.

    _____

    _____

Assessment for Chapter 12:
Research: Documented Essay
Test 2

In this test, you'll use the work of John, a student like you, who is writing a documented essay on Shakespeare's early life.

Prewriting

John used a variety of sources. Here are some note cards he made:

Note card 1

Born on April 26, 1564, in Stratford-on-Avon, England, to John Shakespeare and Mary Arden.
Family was relatively well-to-do.
Father had job of collecting fines for the town.
Father listed among the "capital burgesses" of Stratford and gave money for the relief of plague victims in town.

Riverside Shakespeare, p. 1863

Note card 2

Stratford-on-Avon: the town where Shakespeare was born and spent the early part of his life.
Statford was made a corporate borough in 1553, with provisions for a grammar school, which was funded by an endowment so that children were educated free of charge.
Importance of the school is indicated by the salary of the master: twenty pounds per year and a house.

Shakespeare's Life and Art, pp. 15–17

Note card 3

Married Anne Hathaway in November, 1582.
First child, Susanna, born 1583; twins Hamnet and Judith born 1585.
These are the "Lost Years," because little else is known about this period.

http://shakespeareweb.tripod.com

Note card 4

Attended Stratford Grammar School when he was seven years old.
Studied for nine hours a day, especially Latin.

Shakespeare's Life, p. 21

1. Based on the information that he has gathered on these note cards, show how John could narrow his topic by looping for three minutes on the lines below.

_____

_____

_____

_____

_____

2. What purpose for writing should John adopt? Write two details that John should include to accomplish his purpose for writing.

_____

_____

_____

_____

3. What additional information should John research, based on the narrowed topic you have developed? Develop a research plan for John so that he will have a focused method to look for this additional information.

_____

_____

_____

_____

Drafting

4. John is trying to develop his main idea. Underline the main idea that you think is best. On the lines below, explain why you chose it.

> Although William Shakespeare has been regarded as one of the greatest playwrights and poets of the English language, there is little evidence in his early years that he was destined to become so great.
>
> William Shakespeare had an ordinary childhood for the time period in which he lived.
>
> I am going to write about William Shakespeare.
>
> I am going to write about William Shakespeare's early life.

_____

_____

5. Give an example of an idea in John's essay that might be explored throughout a number of paragraphs in a paragraph block. Explain your answer.

_____

_____

6. Which fact from one of John's note cards would support the concept that Shakespeare was exposed to education at an early age?

_____

_____

Revising

Use this paragraph from the body of John's essay to answer questions 7–11.

> It could be said that Shakespeare grew up in a middle-class family in a small town. Shakespeare's father, John, was a collector of fines for the town of Stratford-on-Avon. John was regarded as part of the well-to-do class in the town. Shakespeare received his early education at the prestigious Stratford Grammar School at age seven. Its educator was paid the princely sum of twenty pounds per year. Shakespeare does not appear to have continued his education beyond grammar school.

7. Cross out the details in the paragraph above that are unnecessary. Explain why you crossed out the details on the lines below.

_____

_____

8. Write a topic sentence for the paragraph, and explain where it should go.

   _____

   _____

9. Select two sentences from the paragraph, and rewrite them so that the lengths are varied.

   _____

   _____

   _____

   _____

10. Replace two of the proper nouns in the paragraph with pronouns. Be sure that the pronouns agree with their antecedents. Write the sentences with their pronoun revisions below.

    _____

    _____

    _____

11. A peer reviewer has told John that the paragraph above could be more interesting. Use a detail from one of John's note cards to write a sentence that could be added to the paragraph.

    _____

Editing and Proofreading

12. Which direct quotation from his note cards should John include in the paragraph on Shakespeare's early years? Explain why.

    _____

    _____

13. Give an example of a detail from one of John's note cards that could be included as an indirect quotation in his essay.

    _____

    Paraphrase the detail above.

    _____

Publishing and Presenting

14. How would you classify John's essay, if it were to be put into a class anthology that includes profiles of different individuals?

    _____

    _____

15. What did you learn about John's topic that you had not known before? Explain your answer.

    _____

    _____

Assessment for Chapter 12: Research: Documented Essay
Test 3

In this test, you'll use the work of Monica, a student like you, who is writing a documented essay on Joan Miro and his role in developing surrealism.

Prewriting

Monica used a variety of sources. Here are some note cards she made:

Note card 1

Surrealism: term first used by Appollinaire; "based on the belief in the superior reality of certain forms of association, such as those produced in dreams."

Definition was developed by André Breton. At the time this definition was developed, no surrealist painting existed.

Artists who were associated with surrealism also included Man Ray, Duchamp, Magritte

Rubin, Dada, Surrealism, and Its Heritage, p. 65

Note card 2

Surrealist painting emerged between 1924 and 1929.

Painters like Magritte tried to fix dream-inspired images onto the canvas.

Even if such paintings appear abstract, they always refer to a subject.

First phase of surrealistic painting was abstract.

Miró switched from cubism to fantasy art in 1924, influenced by Breton's writing.

The Illustrated Books: Catalogue Raisonne, p. 501.

Note card 3

Miró—considerable success as a decorative cubist, but was frustrated by its limitations.

He felt liberated by surrealism.

"He thought it would enable him to realize poetry in visual form."

The Roots of Miró, p. 396

Note card 4

One example of Miró's switch to surrealism seen in his painting The Tilled Field.

The lizard in the dunce cap who is reading a newspaper and the giant ear and eye that grow out of the tree's trunk and leaves have surrealist undertones.

Miró felt that surrealism provided him with a freer alternative to picture painting.

Joan Miró, p. 189

1. Based on the information that she has gathered on these note cards, show how Monica could narrow her topic by looping for five minutes on the lines below.

_____

_____

_____

_____

_____

2. In what area does Monica need to do more research? Write a research plan for Monica so that she will be able to complete the research in a focused manner.

Topic: _____

Question: _____

Plan: _____

3. What other types of sources should Monica consult in order to gather more information about her topic? Why?

_____

_____

_____

Drafting

4. Monica is trying to develop her main idea. Provide a sentence that would sum up a main idea with which she could introduce her essay.

_____

Now, explain why you think this is a good main idea.

_____

_____

5. Give an example of an idea in Monica's essay that might be explored throughout a number of paragraphs in a paragraph block. Explain your answer.

_____

_____

6. Which fact from one of Monica's note cards would support a paragraph about Miró's relationship to surrealism? Explain your answer.

_____

_____

Revising

Use the paragraph from the body of Monica's essay to answer questions 7–11 below.

Miró was converted to surrealism through his friends and the literature of André Breton. He felt free. Even though he enjoyed a lot of success as a cubist, he was upset by the artistic limitations that he felt the doctrine placed on him. His painting *The Tilled Field* is a good example of Miró's switch from cubism to surrealism. The lizard in the dunce cap who is reading a newspaper and the giant ear and eye that grow out of the tree's trunk and leaves have surrealist undertones.

7. Write a topic sentence for the paragraph, and explain where it should go.

_____

_____

8. Which sentence could be eliminated from the paragraph without affecting its coherence? Explain your answer.

_____

_____

9. Choose two words in the paragraph that could be revised to better convey Miró's feelings about cubism and surrealism. Then, on the line below, write the words that you would insert in their place.

_____

10. What are the connotations of the words that you inserted into the paragraph? Why did you select words with these connotations?

   _____

   _____

11. A peer reviewer has told Monica that the paragraph above could be more interesting. Use a detail from one of Monica's note cards to write a sentence that could be added to the paragraph.

   _____

Editing and Proofreading

12. Explain where a direct quotation from one of Monica's note cards could be placed in the paragraph above. Write a sentence that includes the quotation, and make sure to punctuate it correctly.

   _____

   _____

13. Give an example of a detail from one of Monica's note cards that could be listed as an indirect quotation.

   _____

   Paraphrase the detail above.

   _____

Publishing and Presenting

14. Give an example of a teacher who might be interested in having Monica present this documented essay in his or her class. Explain why.

   _____

   _____

   _____

15. If you had to do research for this documented essay, would you use an approach that differed from the one Monica used? Why or why not?

   _____

   _____

   _____

Assessment for Chapter 13:
Research: Research Paper
Test 1

In this test, you will use the work of Frank, a student like you, who is writing a research paper on baseball.

Prewriting

Frank used a variety of sources. Here are some note cards he made:

Note card 1

Original rules of baseball date from 1845.

Called Knickerbocker rules, because that is the name the team gave themselves on the day that they ratified these rules.

There are a total of twenty rules that have evolved into today's rules.

Some interesting rules include: "Members must strictly observe the time agreed on for exercise, and be punctual in their attendance," "A ball knocked out of the field, or outside the range of the first and third base, is foul."

wysiwyg://35/http://baseball-almanac.com/rule11.shtml

Note card 2

A baseball myth: Alexander Doubleday did not invent baseball.

A. G. Spaulding, a business tycoon, did not like the fact that baseball descended from an English game. In 1904, he initiated an investigation that by 1908 concluded that Alexander Doubleday invented it in Cooperstown, NY, in 1839.

"The ancestor of baseball was said to be a U.S. children's game, old cat, called one-cat, two-cat, etc., depending on the number of players. This revisionist interpretation was widely accepted until 1939, when investigations revealed the essentially mythical nature of the theory."

Encyclopaedia Britannica, vol. 2, p. 106.

Note card 3

Baseball first appeared on college campuses during the late 18th century.

Princeton had a "no ball" rule because the students would throw the ball against the president's house and disturb him.

University of North Carolina banned most sports from its campus in the 1790's, but not baseball.

Baseball: The People's Game, pp. 131–132.

Note card 4

Originally from rounders, an English game, similar to modern baseball.

Played on a diamond-shaped field with bases at each corner; batter hits a pitched ball; if ball is hit through or over infield, batter is allowed to run; three missed balls are equal to three strikes. Three strikes equal one out.

1876—baseball established the national league of professional baseball clubs. Baseball began as a business at this point.

The Minors, p. 7.

1. Use the information from Frank's note cards to draw a web that will help Frank to narrow his topic.

2. If Frank's audience is going to include students who are unfamiliar with the game of baseball, what kinds of details should he include in his paper?

_____

_____

_____

3. Use the T-chart below to help Frank develop a plan to continue his research. Write two additional questions he should research and the sources he could consult.

WHAT I WANT TO FIND OUT	POSSIBLE SOURCES

Drafting

4. Underline the statement below that best expresses a thesis statement for Frank's research paper.

Baseball is a great sport that has been played for a long time.

Baseball is an American sport with a long history.

The game of baseball as we know it today has evolved from an early English version of the game.

Baseball is my favorite sport—here's why.

5. Circle the method of organization that Frank should use. On the lines, explain why it will be an effective way to construct his paper.

Order of Importance   Chronological Order

_____

_____

6. Outline Frank's essay, using the information from the note cards.

I. _____

  A. _____

  B. _____

II. _____

  A. _____

  B. _____

Revising

Use the paragraph below to answer questions 7–11.

> Rounders was an English game. Baseball appears to have originated from rounders. Rounders has many similarities to modern baseball. Rounders was played on a diamond-shaped infield with a base at each corner. The batter was pitched a ball. If he hit the ball through or over the infield, he could run.

7. Underline the question or questions below that Frank has to answer in order to provide more complete information in this paragraph. Explain your answer.

   When was rounders invented?
   When was rounders popular in England?
   How did rounders make its way to the U.S.?

   _____
   _____

8. Use the T-R-I structure to label the function of the following sentence from the paragraph.

   Rounders has many similarities to baseball.

   _____

9. Use the Q-A method to write a question and an answer that could represent another way to approach the writing of this paragraph.

   _____
   _____

10. Rewrite two sentences in the paragraph so that they vary in length.

   _____
   _____
   _____
   _____

11. A peer reviewer has told Frank that the organization of this paragraph could be improved. Suggest one change that Frank should make.

   _____
   _____

Editing and Proofreading

Use the following paragraphs to answer questions 12 and 13.

> A. G. Spaulding, who made his fortune in sporting goods, felt that it was shameful that American baseball had its roots in an English game. As a result of these feelings, in 1908 the commission sponsored by Spaulding to investigate the origins of baseball issued a report. The report concluded that the game was invented by Alexander Doubleday in Cooperstown, NY, in 1839.
>
> ''The ancestor of baseball was said to be a U.S. children's game, old cat, called one-cat, two-cat, etc., depending on the number of players. This revisionist interpretation was widely accepted until 1939, when investigations revealed the essentially mythical nature of the theory.'' However, the myth is still popular today.

12. Locate the direct quotation, and explain how it should be set off in the paragraph.

_____

_____

13. Below is the information that Frank compiled on his source card for the encyclopaedia in which he found the quotation. Use this information to write a parenthetical, MLA-style reference.
Encyclopaedia Britannica, vol. 2. p. 160, New York: 1995.

_____

Publishing and Presenting

14. Give an example of a visual aid Frank might use if he were to present his research paper to the class.

_____

_____

15. What did you learn about Frank's topic that you did not know before?

_____

_____

Assessment for Chapter 13: Research: Research Paper
Test 2

In this test, you will use the work of Elizabeth, a student like you, who is writing a research paper on Pablo Picasso.

Prewriting

Elizabeth used a variety of sources. Here are some note cards she made:

Note card 1

Cubism—art movement, primarily dealing with painting, that originated around 1907 in Paris.

Picasso is credited, along with a few other artists, with starting this movement.

It was an intellectual revolt against sensual and emotional art of this era.

"Cubists used analytical systems in which three-dimensional subjects were fragmented from several points of view at the same time."

From 1907 to 1912, this movement was known as concept realism, in which objects are presented as the mind, not the eye, would see them.

1913–1920: known as the synthetic phase. Works created with fewer and simpler forms and painted in brighter colors.

Source: http:// www.encyclopedia.com/articles/03312.html

Note card 2

Picasso exhibited artistic ability even as a young boy.

In 1895, when Picasso was 14 years old, his family moved to Barcelona.

He attended La Lonja, the school of fine arts there.

In 1897, he attended the Royal Academy of Fine Arts of San Fernando in Madrid.

He began to make his first visits to Paris in 1900. He settled in Paris permanently in 1904.

Picasso's artistic style varied considerably during these years.

Pablo Picasso, p. 489.

Note card 3

Picasso's 1907 painting Les Demoiselles D'Avignon signifies his break with impressionists and signals the advent of cubism. He was influenced by Greco-Iberian art and by African sculpture.

Continued to work on his cubist style until 1925, when he switched to a more surrealistic style.

Picasso's Picassos, p. 253.

Note card 4

During the Spanish Civil War, Picasso was inspired to paint Guernica, a painting that expressed the artist's position against the war. During the postwar years, much of Picasso's work centered on themes of war and peace.

Sabartes, J. Pablo Picasso, p. 133.

1. Use the information from Elizabeth's note cards to draw a web that will help her to narrow her topic.

2. Use the T-chart below to help Elizabeth develop a plan to continue her research. Write two additional questions she should research and the sources she could consult.

WHAT I WANT TO FIND OUT	POSSIBLE SOURCES

3. Elizabeth has used a Web site, a book, an encyclopedia, and a magazine article to research her topic so far. Whom might she interview to gain more information about her topic, and why?

_____

_____

Drafting

4. Write a statement that could be used as a thesis statement for Elizabeth's research paper.

_____

5. What sort of organization should Elizabeth use—chronological, cause-and-effect, or order-of-importance? Explain your answer.

_____

_____

6. Create an outline for Elizabeth's paper, using the information that Elizabeth has gathered thus far and the organizational method that you have selected for her.

_____

_____

_____

_____

Revising

Use the following paragraph to answer questions 7–11:

> Picasso developed cubism. You could tell that he switched to this artistic philosophy in one of his paintings from that period. It was the turn of the century. Picasso continued to perfect this style for several years. At that point, you could tell that he switched to a more surrealist style.

7. Use the T-R-I method to write a sentence that illustrates information from the paragraph. (If you need to, go back to one of the note cards for the appropriate information.)

_____

8. Use the Q-A method to write a question and an answer that could represent another way to approach the writing of this paragraph.

    _____

    _____

9. Rewrite two sentences in the paragraph so that they vary in length.

    _____

    _____

    _____

    _____

10. Change two sentences in the paragraph so that they are written in the third person.

    _____

    _____

11. A peer reviewer has told Elizabeth that the organization of this paragraph could be improved. Suggest one change that Elizabeth should make, either by changing the placement of a sentence or rewriting a sentence.

    _____

Editing and Proofreading

Use the paragraph below to answer questions 12 and 13.

> Picasso is credited with being one of the integral artists to begin the cubist movement. "Cubists used analytic systems, in which three-dimensional subjects were fragmented from several points of view at the same time." From 1907 to 1912, Picasso's cubism was also known as concept realism, because it attempted to describe objects in the way that they would be pictured in the mind, not the way that they are observed by the human eye.

12. How should the direct quotation be set off from the rest of the paragraph?

    _____

13. Give an example of a detail from one of Elizabeth's note cards that could be listed as an indirect quotation, and paraphrase it.

    _____

Publishing and Presenting

14. What kind of Web site would be a good place for Elizabeth to publish her research paper electronically?

    _____

    _____

15. If Elizabeth had to write this paper again, what would you suggest that she do differently?

    _____

    _____

**Assessment for Chapter 13:
Research: Research Paper**
Test 3

In this test, you will use the work of Harrison, a student like you, who is writing a research paper on the Cold War.

Prewriting

Harrison used a variety of sources. Here are some note cards he made:

Note card 1

Cold War—term used to describe the conflict between the U.S. and its allies and the U.S.S.R.

Took place after World War II (mid-1940's).

The term was first used by Walter Lippmann in a 1947 book that he wrote about this relationship.

He stated that the relationship between the U.S.S.R. and the U.S. and its allies had "deteriorated to the point of war without a war."

"Cold War." Microsoft Encarta Online

http://encarta.msn.com

Note card 2

Hostility between the U.S. and U.S.S.R. really began at the end of World War I.

"In 1918, the U.S., along with Britain, France, and Japan, intervened militarily in Russia. They did so to restore the collapsed Eastern Front in their war against Germany; however, to Lenin and his colleagues the intervention represented an assault on Russia's feeble new revolutionary regime."

Rethinking the Cold War, p. 27.

Note card 3

Grand Alliance—U.S., Great Britain, and U.S.S.R. allied to defeat Germany during World War II. This alliance was a wary one. The U.S.S.R. charged that it had to spend more money than other allied nations.

Parting the Curtain: Propaganda, Culture, and the Cold War, 1945–1961, p. 102.

Note card 4

May 1945: U.S. and U.S.S.R. were in disagreement over the political future of Poland.

Stalin wanted to control Poland so that it would serve as a buffer zone for the U.S.S.R. The U.S. and its allies opposed this. The U.S. accused the U.S.S.R. of trying to extend its communist influence, while the Soviets argued that the U.S. was trying to stop revolutionary activity where it sprang up.

1947: Truman Doctrine issued by U.S., to aid anticommunist forces in Greece and Turkey

http://coldwar.org

1. Use the information from Harrison's note cards to draw a web that will help him to narrow his topic.

2. Use the T-chart below to create a research plan that would aid Harrison in examining three additional areas in his research. Explain why you selected these three areas.

WHAT I WANT TO FIND OUT	POSSIBLE SOURCES

3. What additional sources should Harrison consider using for his research? Explain your answer.

_____

_____

Drafting

4. Write a statement that could be used as a thesis statement for Harrison's research paper.

_____

5. What method of organization should Harrison use? Why?

_____

_____

_____

6. Create an outline for Harrison's paper using the information that Harrison has gathered thus far and the organizational method that you have selected for him.

_____

_____

_____

_____

_____

_____

Revising

Use the paragraph below to answer questions 7–11.

"Cold War" is a term coined by journalist Walter Lippmann. He coined it in 1947. It refers to the relationship between the U.S.S.R. and the U.S. and its allies just after World War II and until the late 1980's, when the Berlin Wall fell.

7. What information from the note cards could be used to illustrate the main idea in the paragraph?

_____

_____

8. Revise the paragraph so that it follows a Q-A format.

_____

_____

_____

9. Revise two sentences in the paragraph in order to provide variety in sentence structure.

_____

10. Write a thesis statement for the paragraph. Where would be the most effective place to insert it, and why?

_____

_____

11. A peer reviewer told Harrison that he needs to document one of his sources for the paragraph. Explain how the peer reviewer knew this.

_____

_____

Editing and Proofreading

Use the paragraph below to answer questions 12 and 13.

The origins of the hostility between the U.S. and U.S.S.R. really began at the end of World War I. Although "Cold War" did not become a known term until after World War II, the early twentieth century saw trouble brewing between the two superpowers, involving other countries in their dispute.

12. Find a direct quotation on one of Harrison's note cards about the origins of the Cold War. Where would you incorporate it in the above paragraph? Explain your answer.

_____

_____

13. Explain how the direct quotation you chose would be formatted.

_____

_____

Publishing and Presenting

14. What sort of visual aid might Harrison use if he were to present his research paper orally? Why?

_____

_____

15. What might Harrison do differently if he were to rewrite his paper?

_____

_____

Assessment for Chapter 14: Response to Literature
Test 1

In this test, you will be asked to draft a three-paragraph response to a poem. Imagine that you are writing in your reading journal about your reactions to Sonnet 43 by Elizabeth Barrett Browning. Show your understanding of the poem, and describe the ways in which it is meaningful to you.

Sonnet 43

How do I love thee? Let me count the ways.
I love thee to the depth and breadth and height
My soul can reach, when feeling out of sight
For the ends of Being and ideal Grace.
I love thee to the level of every day's
Most quiet need, by sun and candlelight.
I love thee freely, as men strive for Right;
I love thee purely, as they turn from Praise.
I love thee with the passion put to use
In my old griefs, and with my childhood's faith.
I love thee with a love I seemed to lose
With my lost saints—I love thee with the breath,
Smiles, tears, of all my life—and, if God choose,
I shall but love thee better after death.
                    —Elizabeth Barrett Browning

Prewriting

1. Use looping for about three minutes to identify key ideas on which you will base your response.

_____

_____

_____

_____

What is your narrowed topic?

_____

2. If your teacher is the audience for this response, what will his or her expectations be?

_____

Describe the writing style, formal or informal, you will use for this audience.

_____

3. Use the hexagonal strategy chart below to gather details that will support your response. (All levels may not apply to your topic.)

_____

_____

_____   _____

_____   _____

_____   _____

_____   _____

_____

_____

Drafting

4. Use Nestorian organization to outline the ideas you plan to discuss in your response.

I. _____

  A. _____

  B. _____

II. _____

  A. _____

  B. _____

III. _____

  A. _____

  B. _____

5. Write two lines from the poem that support your interpretation of it. Explain why these lines support your points.

_____

_____

_____

_____

6. What is the poet's tone in "Sonnet 43"?

_____

Which line or lines can you cite to support your answer?

_____

_____

7. On a separate sheet of paper, use your notes and information from the graphic organizer to draft your response.

Revising

8. Write the most important idea of your response here.

_____

Rearrange your draft so that your most important idea is in the concluding paragraph, and indicate the change below. If you have no changes you need to make in the arrangement of your ideas, write *none*.

_____

9. Underline the digression in the paragraph below.

One purpose of poetry is to stimulate our minds to think in new ways. Another purpose might be to awaken our hearts. I especially enjoy the symmetry of sonnets. All in all, the experience of reading poetry can feel expansive and enriching for both the mind and the soul.

Now, review your draft. Write any digressions below, and eliminate them from your draft. If you have no digressions, write *none*.

_____

10. Insert the correct comparative or superlative word in the blanks below.

John Donne uses vivid imagery to create a romantic atmosphere in "A Valediction Forbidding Mourning." Donne's decision to have the speaker address the beloved is the _____ effective way to create an aura of romance. Lines such as "So let us meet and make no noise" illustrate the speaker's deep affection for his beloved, while lines such as "Moving of th' earth brings harms and fears" are _____ descriptive of the environment than of the speaker's emotions.

Now, review your draft. Correct any misuse of superlative or comparative forms on the lines below. If your draft does not contain these errors, write *none*.

_____

11. Circle the words below that are dull or vague, and write more vivid, effective words above them.

Emily Dickinson's poems are short but interesting. She writes about normal subjects in order to provide new insights into human experience.

Now, examine your draft. List any dull words that you find, along with more effective replacements, on the lines below.

_____

_____

Editing and Proofreading

12. Correct any errors in the use of underlining and quotation marks in the sentences below.

> Although many students have read Shakespeare's Romeo and Juliet, few have read Henry IV.
>
> William Butler Yeats's poem When You Are Old is also rarely taught in high school.

Now, review your draft. On the lines below, correct any errors in the use of underlining or quotation marks. If your draft does not contain these errors, write *none*.

_____

13. Evaluate your draft according to the rubric below. List any changes that you may need to make to improve your response.

	Score 4	Score 3	Score 2	Score 1
Audience and Purpose	Presents sufficient background on the work(s); presents the writer's reactions forcefully	Presents background on the work(s); presents the writer's reactions clearly	Presents some background on the work(s); presents the writer's reactions at points	Presents little or no background on the work(s); presents few of the writer's reactions
Organization	Presents points in logical order, smoothly connecting them to the overall focus	Presents points in logical order and connects them to the overall focus	Organizes points poorly in places; connects some points to an overall focus	Presents information in a scattered, disorganized manner
Elaboration	Supports reactions and evaluations with elaborated reasons and well-chosen examples	Supports reactions and evaluations with specific reasons and examples	Supports some reactions and evaluations with reasons and examples	Offers little support for reactions and evaluations
Use of Language	Shows overall clarity and fluency; uses precise, evaluative words; makes few mechanical errors	Shows good sentence variety; uses some precise evaluative terms; makes some mechanical errors	Uses awkward or overly simple sentence structures and vague evaluative terms; makes many mechanical errors	Presents incomplete thoughts; makes mechanical errors that cause confusion

_____

_____

_____

_____

Publishing and Presenting

14. If you were to read your response to a small group, what would those in the group say are the most important ideas?

_____

_____

15. Reflect on the aspects of the poem that became clearer to you as you wrote about them.

_____

_____

Assessment for Chapter 14: Response to Literature
Test 2

In this test, you will be asked to draft a three-paragraph literary analysis in response to the poem "Holy Sonnet 10" by John Donne. Your analysis should reflect your understanding of the poem's theme.

Holy Sonnet 10

Death be not proud, though some have called thee
Mighty and dreadful, for thou art not so;
For those whom thou think'st thou dost overthrow,
Die not, poor death, nor yet canst thou kill me.
From rest and sleep, which but thy pictures be,
Much pleasure; then from thee much more must flow,
And soonest our best men with thee do go,
Rest of their bones, and soul's delivery.
Thou art slave to fate, chance, kings, and desperate men,
And dost with poison, war, and sickness dwell,
And poppy [opium], or charms can make us sleep as well
And better than thy stroke; why swell'st [swell with pride] thou then?
One short sleep past, we wake eternally,
And death shall be no more: Death, thou shalt die.

—John Donne

Prewriting

1. Use looping for about three minutes to identify key ideas on which you will base your analysis.

_____

_____

_____

_____

_____

2. If other students are the audience for this analysis, what will their expectations be?

_____

Describe the writing style you will use for this audience.

_____

3. Use the hexagonal strategy chart below to gather details that will support your analysis. (All may not apply to your topic.)

_____

_____

_____   _____

_____   _____

```
              Evaluation
         Plot          Literary
                       Allusions

      Personal         Literary
      Allusions        Devices
              Theme
```

_____

_____

Drafting

4. Use Nestorian organization to outline the ideas you plan to discuss in your analysis.

   I. _____

      A. _____

      B. _____

   II. _____

      A. _____

      B. _____

   III. _____

      A. _____

      B. _____

5. Cite two passages from the poem, and explain how these passages support two points in your analysis.

   _____

   _____

   _____

6. Provide the context for each of the passages that you listed above:

   Passage 1: _____

   Passage 2: _____

7. On a separate sheet of paper, use your notes and information from the graphic organizer to draft your literary analysis.

Name _____

Revising

8. Underline the digression in the paragraph below.

"The Rose" is a story about how Lizzie, the main character, comes of age due to her encounter with a miserable old woman. The rose represents Lizzie's realization that she has matured. Before she met Old Woman Brown, Lizzie was naive about the complexities of life. When she first meets Old Woman Brown, Lizzie is puzzled by her truculence, but she soon learns that this disposition is only a cover for the old woman's sensitive nature.

Now, review your draft. Write any digressions below, and eliminate them from your draft. If you have no digressions, write *none*.

_____

_____

9. Draw a box around the things that are being compared below. On the lines, write the correct form of the comparative and superlative words.

Of the three women in *The Bean Trees*, Mattie is the stronger mother figure. She helps both Taylor and Lou Ann with the difficulties of raising a family and making ends meet. Mattie is also the older and more experienced woman in the novel, and she uses this experience to make wise decisions about her future.

_____

Now, review your draft. Correct any misuse of superlative or comparative terms on the lines below. If your draft does not contain these errors, write *none*.

_____

10. Circle the words below that are dull or vague, and write more vivid, effective words above them.

The Bean Trees is a good book. It deals with hard ideas about the meaning of family. Because their lives are so rough, many of the characters work together and help each other through their most difficult times.

Now, examine your draft. List any dull words that you find, along with more effective replacements, on the lines below. If you do not find any, write *none*.

_____

_____

11. On the lines below, write two questions you would ask a peer about your draft.

_____

_____

_____

_____

Editing and Proofreading

12. Correct any errors in the use of underlining and quotation marks in the sentences below.

> Arthur Miller's play Death of a Salesman has recently been revived on Broadway. Did you know
>
> that The Necklace has been adapted from a short story into a movie? The old television program
>
> Leave It to Beaver can still be seen on certain channels.

Now, review your draft. On the lines below, correct any errors in the use of underlining or quotation marks. If your draft does not contain these errors, write *none*.

_____

13. Evaluate your draft according to the rubric below. List any changes that you may need to make to improve your analysis.

	Score 4	Score 3	Score 2	Score 1
Audience and Purpose	Presents sufficient background on the work(s); presents the writer's reactions forcefully	Presents background on the work(s); presents the writer's reactions clearly	Presents some background on the work(s); presents the writer's reactions at points	Presents little or no background on the work(s); presents few of the writer's reactions
Organization	Presents points in logical order, smoothly connecting them to the overall focus	Presents points in logical order and connects them to the overall focus	Organizes points poorly in places; connects some points to an overall focus	Presents information in a scattered, disorganized manner
Elaboration	Supports reactions and evaluations with elaborated reasons and well-chosen examples	Supports reactions and evaluations with specific reasons and examples	Supports some reactions and evaluations with reasons and examples	Offers little support for reactions and evaluations
Use of Language	Shows overall clarity and fluency; uses precise, evaluative words; makes few mechanical errors	Shows good sentence variety; uses some precise evaluative terms; makes some mechanical errors	Uses awkward or overly simple sentence structures and vague evaluative terms; makes many mechanical errors	Presents incomplete thoughts; makes mechanical errors that cause confusion

_____
_____
_____
_____

Publishing and Presenting

14. How would you classify your analysis, if you were to present it as part of a class anthology on responses to various kinds of literature?

_____
_____

15. Reflect on the aspects of the work that became clearer to you as you wrote your analysis.

_____
_____
_____

Assessment for Chapter 14: Response to Literature
Test 3

In this test, you will be asked to draft a comparative analysis of three or four paragraphs. Write a comparison/contrast of the two poems below that will identify relevant, instructive similarities and differences.

To an Athlete Dying Young

The time you won your town the race
We chaired you through the marketplace;
Man and boy stood cheering by,
And home we brought you shoulder-high.
Today, the road all runners come,
Shoulder-high we bring you home.
And set you at your threshold down,
Townsman of a stiller town.
Smart lad, to slip betimes away
From fields where glory does not stay
And early though the laurel grows
It withers quicker than the rose.
Eyes the shady night has shut
Cannot see the record cut,
And silence sounds no worse than cheers
After earth has stopped the ears:
Now you will not swell the rout
Of lads that wore their honors out,
Runners whom renown outran
And the name died before the man.
So set, before its echoes fade,
The fleet foot on the sill of shade.
And hold to the low lintel up
The still-defended challenge cup.
And round that early-laureled head
Will flock to gaze the strengthless dead,
And find unwithered on its curls
The garland briefer than a girl's.

—A. E. Housman

Holy Sonnet 10

Death be not proud, though some have called
thee
Mighty and dreadful, for thou art not so;
For those whom thou think'st thou dost
overthrow,
Die not, poor death, nor yet canst thou kill me.
From rest and sleep, which but thy pictures be,
Much pleasure; then from thee much more must
flow,
And soonest our best men with thee do go,
Rest of their bones, and soul's delivery
Thou art slave to fate, chance, kings, and
desperate men,
And dost with poison, war, and sickness dwell,
And poppy, or charms can make us sleep as well
And better than thy stroke; why swell'st thou
then?
One short sleep past, we wake eternally,
And death shall be no more; Death, thou shalt
die.

—John Donne

Prewriting

1. Use the looping technique for five minutes to narrow your topic.

_____

_____

_____

_____

_____

2. Select your audience, and describe the audience's expectations. Identify the specific writing strategies you will use to meet these expectations.

_____

_____

_____

_____

3. Fill in the Venn diagram below to organize your ideas about the similarities and differences between the two poems.

To an Athlete Dying Young   Both   Holy Sonnet 10

Drafting

4. Use Nestorian organization to organize the parts of your comparative analysis. Explain why you organized the analysis in the way that you did.

_____

_____

_____

_____

_____

_____

_____

_____

5. Cite one passage from each piece that you will use, and explain how those passages elaborate on an important idea.

_____

_____

_____

_____

_____

_____

_____

_____

_____

_____

6. Briefly provide the context for each passage that you listed above.
Passage 1:

_____

_____

Passage 2:

_____

_____

7. On a separate sheet of paper, use your notes and information from the graphic organizer to draft your comparative analysis.

Revising

8. Write the most important idea of your comparative analysis here.

_____

Rearrange your draft so that your most important idea is in the concluding paragraph. If you have no changes you need to make in the arrangement of your ideas, write *none*.

_____

9. Review your draft. Find a sentence that digresses from the topic sentence in one of your paragraphs. Improve it here, so that it supports the topic sentence.

_____

10. Using the facts below, write a short passage evaluating which of the two candidates for head camp counselor should get the job. Use three comparative or superlative words in your paragraph, and underline them.

   John: John has worked at the camp for two consecutive summers. He has taken on added responsibilities this year, including training new counselors. He has recently become certified to teach art to elementary students.

   Margaret: This is Margaret's first year as a camp counselor. She works at a day-care center during the year, and worked as a baby sitter for small groups of children when she was in high school.

_____

_____

_____

_____

_____

Now, review your draft. Correct any misuse of superlative or comparative terms on the lines below. If your draft does not contain these errors, write *none*.

_____

11. A peer reviewer has commented that he sees passages in your writing that are confusing. Do you agree, and if so, how could you improve your writing?

_____

_____

_____

Editing and Proofreading

12. Correct any errors in the use of underlining and quotation marks in the sentences below.

   In The Bean Trees, the turning point of the novel occurs in the chapter entitled Soundness of Mind and Freedom of Will.

   The short story Dare's Gift can be found in the anthology The Book of Southern Short Stories.

   The movie Inherit the Wind is, in many ways, unlike the play.

Now, review your draft. On the lines below, correct any errors in the use of underlining or quotation marks. If your draft does not contain these errors, write *none*.

_____

13. Evaluate your draft according to the rubric below. List any changes that you may need to make to improve your analysis.

	Score 4	Score 3	Score 2	Score 1
Audience and Purpose	Presents sufficient background on the work(s); presents the writer's reactions forcefully	Presents background on the work(s); presents the writer's reactions clearly	Presents some background on the work(s); presents the writer's reactions at points	Presents little or no background on the work(s); presents few of the writer's reactions
Organization	Presents points in logical order, smoothly connecting them to the overall focus	Presents points in logical order and connects them to the overall focus	Organizes points poorly in places; connects some points to an overall focus	Presents information in a scattered, disorganized manner
Elaboration	Supports reactions and evaluations with elaborated reasons and well-chosen examples	Supports reactions and evaluations with specific reasons and examples	Supports some reactions and evaluations with reasons and examples	Offers little support for reactions and evaluations
Use of Language	Shows overall clarity and fluency; uses precise, evaluative words; makes few mechanical errors	Shows good sentence variety; uses some precise evaluative terms; makes some mechanical errors	Uses awkward or overly simple sentence structures and vague evaluative terms; makes many mechanical errors	Presents incomplete thoughts; makes mechanical errors that cause confusion

_____

_____

_____

_____

Publishing and Presenting

14. Imagine that you are sharing your work with a group of students. How would you summarize the most important ideas from your analysis?

_____

_____

15. How did your analysis of the two works develop as you progressed from reading them to writing about them?

_____

_____

Assessment for Chapter 15: Writing for Assessment
Test 1

In this test, you will be asked to write three paragraphs in which you argue for or against a controversial issue. Consider one of the following topics to help you develop an idea for your essay:

- In a letter to the editor, argue for or against raising the legal driving age to eighteen.
- In a letter to the mayor or city council, argue for or against the decision to allow the construction of a shopping mall on the site of an abandoned farm.
- In an essay, argue for or against the establishment and enforcement of a stricter school dress code.

Write your topic on the line below.

_____

Prewriting

1. Write the key words in one of the writing prompts that show what you are being asked to do in your writing.

_____

2. Write the main idea for your essay on the line below.

_____

3. Based on the information provided in the prompt, identify the audience and your purpose for writing.

My audience is _____

My purpose is _____

Drafting

4. Based on your topic, which kind of organizational structure will you use: comparison and contrast, chronological, or Nestorian? Explain your answer.

_____

_____

5. Give an example of a detail that will support your position effectively.

_____

6. Give an example of a detail you could use to help you illustrate your point clearly.

_____

_____

_____

_____

7. On a separate sheet of paper, use your notes and information from the items above to draft your letter or essay.

Revising

8. Rewrite the first sentence of the introduction below so that it will grab the interest of the reader.

> I think the community service requirement is a good idea. It will only result in positive outcomes for the students and the community. Students will learn about the importance of helping those who are less fortunate than they, and the people they assist will make connections with "real-world" community members. Community service will also save the town money, because the town does not have to pay the students for their services.

_____

Now, on the line below, rewrite the first sentence of your draft to make it more compelling.

_____

9. Cross out the information that detracts from the unity of the paragraph.

> Requiring students to volunteer at local charitable organizations will bring them into contact with people who are different from them. In this way, students will learn about various kinds of people and develop a respect for them. I once volunteered at a senior citizens' center and learned a great deal about what it was like to live during the Depression. Such experiences will only contribute to community unity.

Now, write a sentence from one of your paragraphs that should be deleted for unity. If you do not need to make such a revision, write *none*.

_____

10. Cross out all verbs that are not written in the present tense. Write them correctly above the crossed-out words.

> In addition, community service promoted a sense of achievement in the students. Many students did not think that they were able to make a difference in other people's lives. Without mandatory community service, they never bothered to find out.

Now, correct verb tense errors from your draft on the line below. If your draft contains no errors in verb tense, write *none*.

_____

11. Add the appropriate transition in each blank below.

> Volunteer work helps people who are in need by providing them with needed services. _____, it helps the volunteers by exposing them to the gratifying work of helping others.
>
> _____, I support the board proposal that volunteer work should be required before students earn their high school diplomas.

Now, add a transition to a sentence in your draft to help indicate the relationship between two ideas. Rewrite the sentence below.

_____

Editing and Proofreading

12. Circle each misspelled homophone in the sentences below, and write the correct spelling above it.

   Its important to teach our young people that helping the less fortunate helps our community.

   Each day, we here about many people who are suffering because their unable to get the services

   they need to improve they're lives.

   Now, correct any misspelled homophones from your draft. If your essay does not contain any
   homophone spelling errors, write *none*.

   _____

13. Evaluate your draft according to the rubric below. List any changes that you may need to make to
   improve your letter or essay.

	Score 4	Score 3	Score 2	Score 1
Audience and Purpose	Uses appropriately formal diction; clearly addresses writing prompt	Uses mostly formal diction; adequately addresses writing prompt	Uses some informal diction; addresses writing prompt	Uses inappropriately informal diction; does not address writing prompt
Organization	Presents a clear, consistent organizational strategy	Presents a clear organizational strategy with few inconsistencies	Presents an inconsistent organizational strategy	Shows a lack of organizational strategy
Elaboration	Provides several ideas to support the thesis; elaborates each idea; links all information to thesis	Provides several ideas to support the thesis; elaborates most ideas with facts, details, or examples; links most information to thesis	Provides some ideas to support the thesis; does not elaborate some ideas; does not link some details to thesis	Provides no thesis; does not elaborate ideas
Use of Language	Uses excellent sentence and vocabulary variety; includes very few mechanical errors	Uses adequate sentence and vocabulary variety; includes few mechanical errors	Uses repetitive sentence structure and vocabulary; includes many mechanical errors	Demonstrates poor use of language; generates confusion; includes many mechanical errors

_____

_____

_____

Publishing and Presenting

14. Your teacher has suggested that you save this letter or essay in your writing portfolio, noting the
   date you wrote it. What might be a possible reason to save this writing?

   _____

15. Explain whether you are satisfied with the writing prompt you chose to respond to.

   _____

   _____

Assessment for Chapter 15: Writing for Assessment
Test 2

In this test, you will be asked to write a cause-and-effect essay about a controversial school issue. Consider one of the following topics to help you develop an idea for your essay:

- Explain how increasing the length of the school day will affect students' learning and achievement.
- Analyze the causes and effects of dropping out of high school.
- Examine the effects of requiring that students learn a second language.

Write your topic on the line below.

_____

Prewriting

1. Write the key words in one of the writing prompts that show what you are being asked to do in your writing.

    _____

2. Write the main idea for your essay on the line below.

    _____

3. Based on the information provided in the prompt, identify the audience and your purpose for writing:

    My audience is _____

    My purpose is _____

Drafting

4. Use Nestorian organization to organize the parts of your essay.

    _____

    _____

    _____

    _____

    _____

5. Give an example of a detail that will support your point effectively.

    _____

    _____

6. Give an example of a detail you could use to help you explain your point clearly.

    _____

    _____

    _____

    _____

7. On a separate sheet of paper, use your notes and information to draft your letter or essay.

Revising

Use the paragraph below to answer questions 8 and 9.

> Limiting the hours that teens work during the school year would be terrible. Teens not only earn money when they work, but they learn the importance of responsibility. Their employers feel that teens are a source of affordable labor to fill their needs. Finally, the local economy benefits from working teens, because they spend their money on goods and services provided by local businesses.

8. Rewrite the opening sentence of the paragraph below so that it is more effective.

_____

Now, rewrite the opening sentence of your essay on the lines below so it will be more compelling.

_____

9. Write a transitional sentence that could be placed at the end of the introduction above to lead into the body of the writing.

_____

Now, examine the introduction of your essay, and write a transitional sentence that you would place at the end of it on the lines below.

_____

Use the paragraph below to answer questions 10 and 11.

> Teenagers will lose a valuable opportunity to gain work experience if the bill limiting their ability to work during the school year is passed. Employers look for experienced candidates to fill their vacancies. I know I would choose an experienced candidate over an inexperienced one. Traditionally, teenagers have gained their work experience through the after-school jobs that they hold during high school. Without this experience, teens lost a competitive edge against the adults with whom they compete for employment.

10. Find the information that detracts from the unity of the paragraph, and write it below.

_____

Now, write a sentence from one of your paragraphs that should be deleted for unity. If you do not need to make such a revision. write *none*.

_____

11. Circle all past-tense verbs in the paragraph, and write their present-tense forms on the lines below.

_____

Now, correct errors in verb tense from your draft on the line below. If your draft contains no errors, write *none*.

_____

Editing and Proofreading

12. Circle each misspelled homophone in the sentence below, and write the correct spelling above it.

> The State Assembly should reconsider this bill and here more testimony about it's potential affects.

Now, correct any misspelled homophones in your draft. If your essay does not contain any homophone spelling errors, write *none*.

_____

© Prentice-Hall, Inc.

13. Evaluate your draft according to the rubric below. List any changes that you may need to make to improve your essay.

	Score 4	Score 3	Score 2	Score 1
Audience and Purpose	Uses appropriately formal diction; clearly addresses writing prompt	Uses mostly formal diction; adequately addresses writing prompt	Uses some informal diction; addresses writing prompt	Uses inappropriately informal diction; does not address writing prompt
Organization	Presents a clear, consistent organizational strategy	Presents a clear organizational strategy with few inconsistencies	Presents an inconsistent organizational strategy	Shows a lack of organizational strategy
Elaboration	Provides several ideas to support the thesis; elaborates each idea; links all information to thesis	Provides several ideas to support the thesis; elaborates most ideas with facts, details, or examples; links most information to thesis	Provides some ideas to support the thesis; does not elaborate some ideas; does not link some details to thesis	Provides no thesis; does not elaborate ideas
Use of Language	Uses excellent sentence and vocabulary variety; includes very few mechanical errors	Uses adequate sentence and vocabulary variety; includes few mechanical errors	Uses repetitive sentence structure and vocabulary; includes many mechanical errors	Demonstrates poor use of language; generates confusion; includes many mechanical errors

_____

_____

_____

_____

Publishing and Presenting

14. How do you think your guidance counselor would respond to this essay? Is it a good example of your writing skills?

_____

_____

15. Describe the stage of the writing process that you found most useful.

_____

_____

Assessment for Chapter 15: Writing for Assessment
Test 3

In this test, you will be asked to write a personal essay of three or four paragraphs about an event or experience that significantly changed your view of the world. Consider one of the following ideas: analyze a special trip; examine the impact of earning your driver's license; or describe the birth of a sibling.

Write your topic on the line below.

_____

Prewriting

1. Write the key words in one of the writing prompts that show what you are being asked to do in your writing.

_____

2. Write the main idea for your essay on the line below.

_____

3. Based on the information provided in the prompt, identify the audience and your purpose for writing.

My audience is _____

My purpose is _____

Drafting

4. Based on your topic, which kind of organizational structure will you use? Explain your answer.

_____

_____

5. Give two examples of details that will define, explain, support, or illustrate your points effectively.

_____

_____

_____

6. Explain why the methods you selected will effectively elaborate on the ideas in your essay.

_____

_____

7. On a separate sheet of paper, use your notes and information to draft your letter or essay.

Revising

8. Review your draft, and add an interest-grabbing sentence to your introductory paragraph.

_____

Write a transitional sentence to lead from the introduction to the body of your draft.

_____

Reword the final sentence in your conclusion to give it more impact.

_____

9. Find a phrase or sentence that detracts from the unity of your essay, and write it here.

    _____

    _____

    What change could you make to fix the unity problem in the phrase or sentence?

    _____

    _____

10. Review the verb tenses in your draft. Explain why you chose a particular verb tense for the verbs in your draft.

    _____

    _____

    If any of your verbs are in an inconsistent tense, rewrite them correctly below. If you have no verb tense errors, write *none*.

    _____

    _____

11. Rewrite the paragraph below, using two transitions to make the connections between the sentences clearer.

    > I have such fond memories of the town of Manzanillo. I always go there when I go to Mexico. On our last trip, we ate lunch at a restaurant that overlooked the harbor. We walked through the section of town that contains many shops which sell silver jewelry. I bought a pair of earrings at one of the shops.

    Now, add two transitions to your draft, and write the two new sentences below.

    _____

    _____

    _____

    _____

Editing and Proofreading

12. Circle each misspelled homophone in the sentence below, and write the correct spelling above it.

    > Their are many cites and sounds to discover in Mexico. They are unlike anything I've ever scene or
    >
    > herd in the northeastern United States, wear I live.

    Now, correct any misspelled homophones from your draft. If your essay does not contain any homophone spelling errors, write *none*.

    _____

13. Evaluate your draft according to the rubric below. List any changes that you may need to make to improve your essay.

	Score 4	Score 3	Score 2	Score 1
Audience and Purpose	Uses appropriately formal diction; clearly addresses writing prompt	Uses mostly formal diction; adequately addresses writing prompt	Uses some informal diction; addresses writing prompt	Uses inappropriately informal diction; does not address writing prompt
Organization	Presents a clear, consistent organizational strategy	Presents a clear organizational strategy with few inconsistencies	Presents an inconsistent organizational strategy	Shows a lack of organizational strategy
Elaboration	Provides several ideas to support the thesis; elaborates each idea; links all information to thesis	Provides several ideas to support the thesis; elaborates most ideas with facts, details, or examples; links most information to thesis	Provides some ideas to support the thesis; does not elaborate some ideas; does not link some details to thesis	Provides no thesis; does not elaborate ideas
Use of Language	Uses excellent sentence and vocabulary variety; includes very few mechanical errors	Uses adequate sentence and vocabulary variety; includes few mechanical errors	Uses repetitive sentence structure and vocabulary; includes many mechanical errors	Demonstrates poor use of language; generates confusion; includes many mechanical errors

_____
_____
_____
_____

Publishing and Presenting

14. What is one reason to save this essay in your writing portfolio, and how does it reflect your writing skills?

_____
_____

15. Reflect on the stage of the writing process that you found most useful as you wrote this essay. Explain your answer.

_____
_____

Assessment for Chapter 16:
Workplace Writing

1. Circle the letter of the answer that contains an example of workplace writing. On the lines, explain why your answer is correct and why the other answers are incorrect.

   a. a poem _____
   _____

   b. a journal entry _____
   _____

   c. a letter to the editor of a newspaper _____
   _____

   d. a letter to a friend in Florida _____
   _____

2. Describe one of the four qualities of effective workplace writing.
   _____
   _____
   _____

3. Explain why it is important that workplace writing be concise.
   _____
   _____
   _____

4. Explain how a business letter differs from a memorandum.
   _____
   _____
   _____

5. Circle the letter of the answer that contains an example of a courteous and formal salutation that you would find in a business letter. On the line, explain why the answer you chose is correct.
   a. Dear Sir:
   b. Dearest Sir:
   c. Hey, Sir!
   d. To whoever ends up reading this letter:
   _____
   _____

6. Rewrite the paragraph below so that it could be used in a cover letter for a person who is looking for a job in a science laboratory.

> Anyway, I think I'd be perfect as your new research assistant. For one thing, I think I have a great G.P.A.—3.7! I also have lots of work experience, and I have taken science classes every year since I was a little kid. This past summer, I learned a ton of research skills. All of these qualities make me a great candidate for your job opening.

_____

_____

_____

_____

7. Imagine that you are writing a letter of complaint to a company about a product that you purchased. Circle the letter of the answer that contains the types of facts you would gather during your prewriting. On the line, explain why the answer you chose is correct.
   a. name of the salesperson who sold you the product and the name of the store where you bought the product
   b. name of the product that you purchased, reasons for your dissatisfaction, place of purchase
   c. color of the salesperson's dress, color of her eyes, name of the department
   d. name of the friend to whom you confided your dissatisfaction with the product

_____

8. Circle the letter of the answer that contains the name of the intended audience for a memorandum. On the line, explain why the answer you chose is correct.
   a. family members
   b. news agency
   c. company employees
   d. community at large

_____

9. Identify the appropriate writing stage for a memorandum that is described in each of the statements below.
   Present your main point clearly and concisely.

_____

   Make sure that you have filled in the TO: and RE: areas correctly.

_____

   Print and distribute your memo.

_____

   Think about audience's knowledge and interest level to gather necessary details.

_____

   Revise inconsistent or confusing formatting.

_____

   Now, write the stages in the appropriate order.

_____

_____

10. Assume you are a vice president of human resources. Write the heading for a short memo, using today's date, to the company employees at Safewell, Inc., about a new vacation policy that will go into effect this summer.

_____
_____
_____
_____
_____

11. Revise the following RE: line:
RE: Why we need to require our employees to upgrade their computer skills.

_____

12. Explain why it is important to present prospective employers with a well-written résumé.

_____
_____

13. Summarize the following information about a candidate's work experience into a résumé entry:

From September 1995 to October 1997, I was the project manager at Rite-Way Advertising. During that time, I made sure that project deadlines were met and that the customer was satisfied with the ads that we developed. I'm a good writer, and I have creative ideas.

_____
_____
_____

14. Imagine that you have a friend who is writing his or her first résumé. What advice would you give to him or her?

_____
_____

15. Explain why it is important to organize information in a résumé under headings that stand out from the rest of the information on the page.

_____
_____

16. What kinds of information would you need to gather during the prewriting stage of preparing a résumé?

_____
_____

17. Explain why you must include a brief message on a fax cover sheet.

_____

18. Explain why it is important to fill in a fax sheet accurately and completely.

_____

19. Circle the letter of the answer that contains an example of a purpose for which you would fill out an application. On the line, explain why the answer you chose is correct.
    a. purchase groceries on-line
    b. change a mailing address
    c. request a different table in a restaurant
    d. search for information on the Internet

    _____

20. Imagine that you are applying for a position for a summer job of your choosing and that you have some experience in this kind of work. Use the space below to fill in a sample application. Include basic contact information, work experience, and personal references. (You may invent information if you need to, for the purposes of filling out this form.)

Job Application

Part II:
Grammar, Usage, and
Mechanics

Grammar, Usage, and Mechanics: Cumulative Diagnostic Test

Part 1: Identifying Parts of Speech

On the line after each sentence, identify the part of speech of each underlined word or group of words in the sentence.

1. <u>Yesterday</u> our class took a <u>field</u> trip <u>to</u> the new Earth and Space Center.

   _____

2. The center <u>is located</u> in a <u>spectacular</u> new building.

   _____

3. Through a <u>series</u> of interactive exhibits, visitors can learn <u>about</u> <u>not only</u> geology <u>but also</u> astronomy.

   _____

4. The exhibits range from the far <u>reaches</u> of the <u>universe</u> to Earth's <u>inner</u> core.

   _____

5. <u>WOW!</u> Did the universe <u>really</u> start <u>out</u> with a Big Bang?

   _____

6. The displays contain <u>up-to-date</u> information in <u>astrophysics</u> and <u>earth</u> science.

   _____

7. <u>Along</u> a spiral walkway <u>outside</u> a gigantic sphere, the history of the universe <u>is chronicled</u>.

   _____

8. <u>Those</u> of <u>us</u> who attended had lots of opportunities for <u>hands-on</u> learning.

   _____

9. Mel and <u>I</u> <u>especially</u> enjoyed the space show, <u>which</u> lasted half an hour.

   _____

10. The center brings <u>together</u> science, architecture, <u>and</u> education in a <u>unique</u> fashion.

    _____

Part 2: Identifying Parts of a Sentence

Follow the directions in brackets at the end of each sentence.

11. The restaurant business is difficult and demanding. [Write the compound predicate adjective.]

    _____

12. Do you know anyone in the restaurant business? [Write the verb.]

    _____

13. Designing the seating area gives owners a chance for creativity. [Write the indirect object.]

    _____

14. There are materials to choose and color schemes to select. [Write the complete subject.]

_____

15. Who likes Chinese food more, Raymond or Trudi? [Write the subject.]

_____

16. One important challenge for a restaurant owner is training a good staff. [Write the predicate nominative.]

_____

17. We all consider those Japanese dishes the very best. [Write the objective complement.]

_____

18. That French restaurant's location gives it an advantage. [Write the direct object.]

_____

19. Some restaurant diners have finicky tastes. [Write the simple subject.]

_____

20. Give me the menu for dessert. [Write the subject.]

_____

Part 3: Identifying Phrases

On the line provided, write whether the underlined portion of each sentence is a *prepositional phrase*, an *appositive phrase*, an *infinitive phrase*, a *participial phrase*, a *nominative absolute*. or a *gerund phrase*.

21. Would you like <u>to visit the Everglades</u> one day? _____

22. The Everglades, <u>an area in southern Florida</u>, comprises one of America's most distinctive ecosystems. _____

23. <u>Stretching south from Lake Okeechobee to Florida Bay</u>, the area is rich in wildlife. _____

24. <u>Preserving this area for future generations</u> has been challenging. _____

25. <u>Overrun by development</u>, half of the original Everglades has vanished. _____

26. <u>Canals and levees having been constructed</u>, the underground distribution of water has changed dramatically. _____

27. At one time, <u>draining land for farms and towns</u> was a high priority. _____

28. Engineers <u>called hydrologists</u> are now attempting to redirect the water flow. _____

29. These specialists hope <u>to restore the ecosystem to a healthy level.</u> _____

30. Perhaps their efforts will have a positive impact <u>on the area.</u> _____

Part 4: Identifying Clauses and Types of Sentences

On the line provided, write whether each sentence is *simple, compound, complex,* or *compound-complex.* If the sentence contains any subordinate clauses, write each subordinate clause and tell whether it is an *adjective clause,* an *adverb clause,* a *noun clause,* or an *elliptical clause.*

31. If you visit the seashore in our region, you may often see river otters playing or feeding.

_____

32. Last spring I observed a pair of adult otters and their young; small river otters are called kits.

_____

33. Sea otters, which weigh more than river otters, never den on land, and they are less social than river otters.

_____

34. The large hind flippers of a sea otter prevent it from matching the river otter's agility on land.

_____

35. A mother and her single offspring, called a pup, are what constitutes the basic unit of sea otter society.

_____

Part 5: Creating Effective Sentences

On the lines provided, rewrite the following sentences according to the directions in brackets.

36. Ramadan is the name of a month. The ninth month of the Islamic calendar. [Correct the sentence error.]

_____

_____

37. Designated as a month for fasting, Muslims adopt a special routine during Ramadan. [Correct the misplaced modifier.]

_____

_____

38. Every day the fast starts at dawn. The precise moment is determined by the point at which one can distinguish a white thread from a black one. [Combine into a compound-complex sentence.]

_____

_____

39. The fast ends each day at sunset, then prayers are said and passages from the Koran are recited. [Correct the sentence error.]

_____

_____

40. According to the Koran, Muslims may not eat during the fast. Neither may they drink during the fast. [Combine using a compound verb.]

_____

_____

41. Young children and very old people are exempted from the fast. [Rewrite using inverted word order.]

_____

_____

42. To determine the dates of holidays, a lunar calendar is used by Muslims. [Correct the dangling modifier.]

_____

_____

43. A special holiday called the Fast-Breaking is observed, ending the month of Ramadan. [Begin the sentence with a participle.]

_____

_____

44. Muslims recite prayers on this day. They also feast. [Combine using a compound predicate.]

_____

_____

45. Have you ever seen pictures of the Blue Mosque in Istanbul, Turkey. [Correct the sentence punctuation.]

_____

_____

Part 6: Supplying the Correct Verb
Circle the verb in parentheses that best completes each sentence.

46. If you (were, will be) to research the origins of the umbrella, you might discover some surprising facts.

47. The umbrella, which (grew, growed) out of the fan, has a 3,000-year history.

48. The first umbrellas (were developed, have developed) in ancient Mesopotamia.

49. Early umbrellas (did not protect, were not protecting) people from the rain but instead shielded them from the scorching sun.

50. As you probably know, the sun (is, be) strong in this region of the Middle East.

51. Ancient Greeks and Romans also (used, will have used) umbrellas as sunshades.

52. Umbrellas were (bore, borne) almost entirely by women, however.

53. In these cultures, umbrellas (seemed, are seeming) to be unmanly for men.

54. Modern umbrellas (became, become) fashionable as raingear only in the late eighteenth century.

55. A Londoner named Jonas Hanway proposed that these accessories (are, be) carried by proper British gentlemen.

Part 7: Supplying the Correct Pronoun
Circle the word in parentheses that best completes each sentence.

56. (Us, We) students elected Matt president of the Drama Society.

57. Paulette objected to (us, our) joining the drama society.

58. When (your, you're) acting in a play, are you ever nervous?

59. Simon sometimes doesn't remember (who's, whose) line comes next.

60. The success of each production is important to us and (them, they).

61. Either John, Iris, or (he, him) will probably get the lead role.

62. Aunt Polly and Uncle Sid always send us (their, they're) best wishes for the production.

63. (Who, Whom), may I ask, is familiar with this play by George Bernard Shaw?

64. Barney and Tom like comedies more than (I, me).

65. The audience included friends, relatives, and people (who, whom) I had never met.

Part 8: Making Words Agree
Circle the term in parentheses that best completes each sentence.

66. Each of my friends (is, are) conscious of good nutrition.

67. There (is, are) no one or nothing that can persuade Jack or Mike to eat sugar.

68. Bacon and eggs, Anna maintains, (is, are) not a healthy choice for breakfast.

69. Most of the time, neither Roberto nor his friends (eat, eats) fast food.

70. Either these magazine articles or that book (furnish, furnishes) helpful information about nutrition.

71. Especially high in fat and cholesterol (is, are) fried foods.

72. Most of our diets today (is, are) too high in fat and sugar.

73. Each person should carefully select a diet suited to (his or her, their) needs.

74. A new interest of theirs (is, are) high-protein diets.

75. Either spinach or broccoli is often singled out for (its, their) nutritional value.

76. Many of the body's nutritional needs (is, are) supplied by fruits and vegetables.

77. Was it Jack or Joe who found a helpful Web site on which to research (his, their) questions on nutrition?

78. Whenever the nutritionist spoke, the audience gave her (its, their) attention.

79. The number of informative articles on nutrition in those newspapers (has, have) been steadily increasing.

80. Dr. Peters is only one of several experts who (has, have) written a book on nutrition.

Part 9: Using Modifiers Correctly
Circle the term in parentheses that best completes each sentence.

81. Some people believe that a marathon tests physical endurance more than (anything, anything else).

82. Perhaps no marathon in history is (famouser, more famous) than the first.

83. At the Battle of Marathon in 490 B.C., the odds were (more bad, worse) than usual for the outnumbered Greeks, yet somehow they won.

84. Of all the Greeks, Pheidippides was the (better, best) runner.

85. Carrying the news of the Greek victory to Athens, Pheidippides ran a bit (farther, further) than twenty-six miles.

86. Few runners are (finer, more fine) than those in the New York Marathon.

87. My hopes of entering the race this year are higher than (Bob, Bob's).

88. Of Craig and Carl, who usually runs (faster, fastest)?

89. Watching thousands of runners massing at the starting line is one of the (grandest, most grandest) spectacles in the world.

90. The tension mounts (farther, further) as the lead runners approach the finish line

Part 10: Eliminating Usage Errors
Circle the term in parentheses that best completes each sentence.

91. Does extreme weather (affect, effect) your area often?

92. The weather prompted discussion (among, between) the many meteorologists with the National Weather Service.

93. (Nowhere, Nowheres) else in the world is the weather as variable as it is in the United States.

94. People can (lose, loose) their property or even their lives as a result of tornadoes.

95. A tornado is quite (different from, different than) a hurricane.

96. Meteorologists are continually refining (their, there) long-range forecasts.

97. However, some scientists maintain that forecasts can't (ever, never) be 100 percent accurate.

98. By the end of October, it is (already, all ready) snowing in some sections of the country.

99. (Being that, Because) farmers depend on predictable weather cycles, irregular patterns can badly hurt agricultural regions.

100. No (fewer, less) than ten thousand thunderstorms occur annually in the United States.

Part 11: Proofreading for Capitalization

On the line after each sentence, rewrite the sentence, correcting errors in capitalization.

101. how much do you know about the city of newport, rhode island?

_____

102. refugees from massachusetts bay colony founded newport in 1639.

_____

103. early in the american revolution, british forces occupied the city.

_____

104. newport is the site of trinity church and touro synagogue.

_____

105. in the nineteenth century, wealthy families like the vanderbilts built mansions there.

_____

106. many of the mansions are now museums maintained by the newport historical society.

_____

107. the america's cup—a sailing race—used to be held in the atlantic ocean off newport.

_____

108. newport's jacqueline bouvier married senator john f. kennedy in september 1953.

_____

109. when kennedy served as president of the united states, mrs. kennedy was a popular first lady.

_____

110. she is noted for supervising the restoration of the white house.

_____

Part 12: Proofreading for Punctuation

Rewrite each sentence, correcting errors in punctuation as necessary.

111. Francisco Goya 1746–1828 one of Spain's greatest painters was born in Fuendetodos.

_____

112. At the age of fourteen Goya was apprenticed to José Luzan and spent four years in Luzans studio.

_____

113. In 1763 however Goya left for Madrid Spain.

_____

114. At the start of his career Goya designed a series of tapestries noted for their grace wit and charm.

_____

115. Rejecting traditional themes Goya depicted open air amusements attended by upper class Spaniards.

_____

116. Goya spent 1771 in Italy and it is clear that he lived for some time in Rome.

_____

117. Goya returned to Spain around 1773 a dozen years later he was appointed court painter.

_____

118. Goyas portraits which do not idealize their subjects show him to be a keen observer.

_____

119. In 1793 a near fatal illness left Goya totally deaf.

_____

120. Goya who favored social reform often portrayed the nobility with a sharp satirical eye.

_____

121. After Napoleon invaded Spain in 1808 Goyas paintings often protested wars savagery.

_____

122. The bloodshed of May 3 1808 is the subject of one of Goyas finest paintings.

_____

123. Goya also completed a powerful series of etchings entitled The Disasters of War.

_____

124. Some of Goyas last works offer frightening almost nightmarish images.

_____

125. Goya lived in self imposed exile in Bordeaux France in the last years of his life.

_____

17 Assessment for Chapter 17: The Parts of Speech

Part 1: Identifying the Types of Nouns

On the line provided, indicate whether each noun is (a) *concrete* or *abstract*, (b) *singular* or *plural*, (c) *collective*, (d) *compound*, and (e) *common* or *proper*.

1. time travel _____

2. skyscraper _____

3. Woodrow Wilson _____

4. jazz _____

5. warfare _____

6. battalion _____

7. submarines _____

8. Armistice Day _____

9. enthusiasm _____

10. brothers-in-law _____

Part 2: Identifying Pronouns and Antecedents

On the lines provided, write the pronouns and their antecedents (if any) in the sentences below. Then, identify each pronoun as *personal, reflexive, intensive, demonstrative, relative, interrogative,* or *indefinite*.

11. Which of the events that led up to World War I made the war itself inevitable?

   _____

   _____

12. Historians identify several factors, but virtually all of those whom you ask point to one immediate cause.

   _____

   _____

13. All of the people agree; they say the assassination of Austria's Archduke Franz Ferdinand on June 28, 1914, triggered the war.

   _____

   _____

14. By early August, Europe found itself at war, but no one thought the conflict would drag on for four long years.

   _____

   _____

15. Americans, who were neutral at first in a war that they felt was not theirs, eventually entered it in 1917.

   _____

   _____

Part 3: Identifying Verbs

On the line after each sentence, write the verb or verb phrase. Then, write *AV* or *LV* to indicate whether it is an action verb or a linking verb and *T* or *I* to indicate whether it is transitive or intransitive.

16. In 1917, Germany attacked American merchant ships.

_____

17. American support for entry into the war was reluctant at best.

_____

18. President Woodrow Wilson described the conflict as a fight for democracy.

_____

19. The appearance of the first American troops in Paris seemed miraculous to the French.

_____

20. Might the Allies have triumphed without American aid?

_____

Part 4: Identifying Modifiers and the Words They Modify

On the line after each sentence, write any *adjectives* or *adverbs* the sentence contains. Indicate whether each modifier is an adjective or an adverb, and also identify the word or words that it modifies.

21. World War I clearly showed that modern technology had changed warfare forever.

_____

_____

22. The invention of heavy artillery was especially decisive.

_____

_____

23. Because of new weaponry, trench warfare was both inevitable and grisly.

_____

_____

_____

24. After only six months of fighting, nearly 500,000 German soldiers lay dead.

_____

_____

_____

25. Almost incredibly, a single battle in 1916 lasted five months.

_____

_____

_____

Part 5: Identifying Conjunctions, Prepositions, and Interjections

In the sentences below, circle any examples of the part of speech indicated in parentheses.

26. During World War I, Russia fought on the side of both the British and the French. (conjunction)

27. Russia, like its allies, had hoped for the war to end quickly, but these hopes were not to be fulfilled. (preposition)

28. Furthermore, the world was stunned as revolution swept Russia in 1917. (conjunctive adverb)

29. Not only did the Russian peasants demand equality, but they also forced Russia from the larger war and into a different type of conflict. (conjunction)

30. Wow! When the powerful Russian monarchy was overthrown by the peasants, it was amazing! (interjection)

Part 6: Words as Different Parts of Speech
On the line after each sentence, identify the part of speech of the underlined word.

31. What would <u>cause</u> America to join the fighting World War I? _____

32. America fought for the <u>cause</u> of democracy. _____

33. How was the American economy affected by the <u>war</u>? _____

34. Many companies produced items for the <u>war</u> effort. _____

35. Thriving industries gave the economy a <u>boost</u>. _____

36. Did the labor shortage <u>boost</u> the availability of jobs for women? _____

37. Before the war, <u>most</u> African Americans lived in the rural South. _____

38. <u>Most</u> of the new job opportunities were in northern cities. _____

39. Many African Americans sought work in the <u>steel</u> industry. _____

40. If necessary, they would <u>steel</u> themselves to harsh living conditions. _____

Part 7: Identifying Parts of Speech
Read this passage. Then, on the appropriately numbered line below the passage, write the part of speech of each underlined word.

(41) <u>Nearly</u> ten million people died in World War I, (42) <u>which</u> lasted for four long years. Ironically, for (43) <u>much</u> of the war, the (44) <u>battle</u> line moved (45) <u>back</u> and forth less than ten miles. One major (46) <u>result</u> of the conflict was to change the old political order. (47) <u>Before</u> the war, continental Europe was dominated by monarchies, (48) <u>and</u> democracy was virtually (49) <u>unknown</u>. After the war, Europe (50) <u>became</u> far more democratic.

41. _____   46. _____

42. _____   47. _____

43. _____   48. _____

44. _____   49. _____

45. _____   50. _____

Part 8: Standardized Test Practice
Directions: Read the following passage and choose the word or group of words that belongs in each space. Circle the letter of your answer.

As men joined the armed forces ____(51)____ World War I, women stepped into some of ____(52)____ jobs. Women received better pay in ____(53)____ industries than they had in peacetime. Still, they earned ____(54)____ than the men they replaced. In factories, women ____(55)____ weapons and airplane parts. Some women drove trolley cars ____(56)____ delivered the mail. The women workers ____(57)____ helped the country run smoothly but they also proved that women could handle a ____(58)____ range of jobs. ____(59)____, after the war ended, most of the gains made ____(60)____ women disappeared.

51 A when
    B during
    C fight
    D had fought

52 F necessary
    G war
    H them
    J their

53 A whomever
    B significantly
    C wartime
    D occasionally

54 F less
    G some
    H salaries
    J as well as

55 A dangerous
    B assembly
    C military
    D assembled

56 F but
    G for
    H or
    J while

57 A both
    B not only
    C only
    D either

58 F efficiently
    G worked
    H necessarily
    J wide

59 A They
    B Unfortunately
    C Wow
    D Never

60 F by
    G nearby
    H throughout
    J forever

18 Assessment for Chapter 18: Basic Sentence Parts

Part 1: Identifying Subjects and Predicates

In each sentence below, draw a vertical line between the complete subject and the complete predicate. Then underline each simple subject once and each simple predicate twice.

1. Body temperature declines dramatically during hibernation.

2. The ground squirrel is a good example of a hibernator.

3. Squirrels prepare for hibernation by doubling their body weight.

4. They dig a deep burrow in the ground.

5. The squirrel then curls itself up inside a small side pocket of the burrow.

6. The animal's heart rate gradually slows down from 350 beats a minute to only 2–4 beats.

7. Body temperatures of hibernating squirrels can drop by as much as 60 degrees Fahrenheit.

8. The squirrel's metabolic activity plunges by 98 percent.

9. Its body temperature inexplicably fluctuates and sometimes returns to normal.

10. Bears and bats also hibernate.

Part 2: Locating Hard-to-Find Subjects

In each sentence, underline the simple subject once and the verb twice. On the line after the sentence, include in parentheses any subject that is understood.

11. There is only one common marsupial in America. _____

12. Can you name it? _____

13. Taking that honor is the Virginia opossum. _____

14. An opossum in its infancy is as tiny as a fingertip. _____

15. Inside its mother's pouch lives the growing infant. _____

16. Sally, tell us about marsupials in Australia. _____

17. Do those include kangaroos and wallabies? _____

18. Here are photos and drawings of a great red kangaroo. _____

19. Look at this photo caption, please. _____

20. What amazing animals live in Australia! _____

Part 3: Identifying Complements

On the line after each sentence, list any complements and indicate whether the complement is a *direct object*, an *indirect object*, an *objective complement*, a *predicate nominative*, or a *predicate adjective*.

21. Ratels, also called honey badgers, are intriguing animals.

_____

22. Native to Africa and Asia, ratels are normally nocturnal.

_____

23. They seldom reveal themselves to human observers.

_____

24. Their black-and-white markings make these animals a vivid study in contrast.

_____

25. A ratel makes its home in a burrow or among rocks.

   _____

26. Scientists consider ratels extremely courageous.

   _____

27. The animal's digging ability is second only to an aardvark's.

   _____

28. Although technically carnivores, ratels eat mostly honey and bee larvae.

   _____

29. The greater honey guide, a type of bird, shows the ratel the location of beehives.

   _____

30. Such cooperation, called mutualism, benefits both species.

   _____

Part 4: Identifying Sentence Parts

On the line after each sentence, identify whether the underlined word is a *simple subject*, a *simple predicate*, a *direct object*, an *indirect object*, an *objective complement*, a *predicate nominative*, or a *predicate adjective*.

31. Most insectlike creatures <u>possess</u> wings and antennae. _____

32. Among the exceptions, however, are <u>spiders</u>. _____

33. Spiders are <u>arachnids</u>, not insects. _____

34. Insects have only six <u>legs</u>. _____

35. In contrast, arachnids possess eight <u>legs</u>. _____

36. Very important to a spider are its <u>spinnerets</u>. _____

37. These organs offer <u>spiders</u> the main means of securing their prey. _____

38. The silk <u>thread</u> from these organs builds webs and cocoons. _____

39. Scientists consider few species of spider <u>dangerous</u>. _____

40. Some spiders, however, are <u>poisonous</u> to humans. _____

Part 5: Standardized Test Practice

Directions: Circle the letter of the best way to write the underlined section. If the underlined section needs no change, circle the letter of the choice "Correct as is."

[41]The platypus is a semiaquatic mammal. Native to eastern Australia. [42]Also called duckbills. Platypuses are strange-looking animals. [43]They have a long, duckbill-shaped muzzle, rubbery ears, and no teeth. [44]Their head, body, and tail are covered with dark brown fur. Feet are webbed. [45]Platypuses hunt small freshwater animals. With the aid of electroreceptors in their bills.

41. A. The platypus is a semiaquatic mammal, it is native to eastern Australia.
    B. The platypus is a semiaquatic native of eastern Australia.
    C. The platypus is a semiaquatic mammal native to eastern Australia.
    D. Correct as is

42. A. Also called duckbills, platypuses are strange-looking animals.
    B. Also called duckbills, and platypuses are strange-looking animals.
    C. Strange-looking animals. Platypuses are also called duckbills.
    D. Correct as is

43. A. They have a long, duckbill-shaped muzzle. They have rubbery ears. And no teeth.
    B. They have a long, duckbill-shaped muzzle, with rubbery ears, and having no teeth.
    C. With a long, duckbill-shaped muzzle, rubbery ears, and no teeth.
    D. Correct as is

44. A. Their head, body, and tail are covered with dark brown fur, their feet are webbed.
    B. They have dark brown fur on their head, body, tail, and webbed feet.
    C. Their head, body, and tail are covered with dark brown fur; their feet are webbed.
    D. Correct as is

45. A. With the aid of electroreceptors in their bills, platypuses hunt small freshwater animals.
    B. Platypuses hunt small freshwater animals, they have electroreceptors in their bills.
    C. Platypuses hunt electroreceptors with the aid of small freshwater animals in their bills.
    D. Correct as is

Assessment for Chapter 19:
Phrases and Clauses

Part 1: Identifying Prepositional Phrases, Appositives, and Appositive Phrases
Identify the underlined phrase in each sentence as an *adjective phrase, adverb phrase,* or *appositive phrase.* Also identify the word or words that each phrase modifies or renames.

1. Nat "King" Cole, <u>a talented jazz singer</u>, won international fame during the 1940's and 1950's.

   _____

2. The daughter <u>of Nat "King" Cole</u>, Natalie Cole was born in 1950.

   _____

3. <u>Like her father</u>, Natalie chose a career in music.

   _____

4. Before beginning her music career, she also studied child psychology <u>at the University of Massachusetts</u>.

   _____

5. Natalie recorded *Inseparable*, <u>her first album</u>, in 1975.

   _____

6. The album earned Natalie several honors, <u>two grammy awards and a gold record</u>.

   _____

7. In 1979, Natalie received a star <u>on the Walk of Fame</u> in Hollywood.

   _____

8. In 1991, Natalie began recording the most acclaimed album of her career, <u>a compilation of her father's best known songs</u>.

   _____

9. The album included a duet <u>with her father</u>.

   _____

10. Natalie sang the song live, accompanied <u>by a recorded sound track</u> of her father's voice.

    _____

Part 2: Identifying Verbals and Verbal Phrases
On the line after each sentence, write whether the underlined word or words are an *infinitive,* an *infinitive phrase,* a *gerund,* a *gerund phrase,* a *participle,* a *participial phrase,* or a *nominative absolute.*

11. <u>Born in Cincinnati, Ohio</u>, Steven Spielberg loved movies as a child. _____

12. <u>Directing</u> became young Spielberg's greatest ambition. _____

13. Soon the young director began <u>to win awards</u>. _____

14. <u>Revolutionizing special effects</u> was one of his great achievements. _____

15. <u>His reputation established by the mid-1970's</u>, Spielberg tackled ever more ambitious

    projects. _____

16. He found that he had many stories <u>to tell</u>. _____

17. His adventure films, though huge box-office draws, had never won him a <u>coveted</u> Academy

    Award. _____

18. It was *Schindler's List*, a <u>riveting</u> epic about the Holocaust, that earned Spielberg his first Best

Picture Oscar. _____

19. <u>Having won the acclaim of his peers for a serious drama</u>, Spielberg returned to adventure films with

Jurassic Park. _____

20. He also continued <u>making serious films like</u> *Amistad* and *Saving Private Ryan*.

_____

Part 3: Identifying Subordinate Clauses

Underline the subordinate clause in each sentence below. Then, on the line after each sentence, identify whether the subordinate clause functions as an *adjective*, an *adverb*, a *noun*, or an *elliptical clause*.

21. Most movie fans know who Barbra Streisand is.

_____

22. Streisand, who was born in Brooklyn, has been a star for decades.

_____

23. Her singing is as well known as her acting.

_____

24. When Streisand was twenty-two, she won rave reviews for her performance as Fanny Brice in *Funny Girl*.

_____

25. Critics wrote that she charmed audiences with her intuitive talent.

_____

26. After *Funny Girl* took Broadway by storm, it became a popular film.

_____

27. Streisand went on to star in several films that were huge hits.

_____

28. To many, however, directing is even more challenging than acting.

_____

29. In 1983, Streisand directed and starred in the film *Yentl*, which is based on a story by Isaac Bashevis Singer.

_____

30. This film, together with *The Prince of Tides* eight years later, proved that Streisand was an extremely talented director.

_____

Part 4: Classifying Sentences by Structure

On the line after each sentence, identify the structure as *simple, compound, complex,* or *compound-complex.*

31. Ludwig van Beethoven, who was born in Germany in 1770, was one of the world's greatest

composers. _____

32. A musical pioneer, Beethoven revolutionized the forms of the symphony and the piano concerto. _____

33. On meeting Beethoven, Mozart predicted that the young composer "would make a noise in the world some day," and Mozart was right. _____

34. When we consider that Beethoven was deaf for over half of his adult life, his achievements are all the more amazing. _____

35. Last week, our class listened to Beethoven's *Eroica* symphony, and some of us also saw a film on his life. _____

Part 5: Standardized Test Practice
Directions: Read each passage. The underlined sections are correctly written sentences that should be combined. Choose the best way to combine each underlined section. Circle the letter of your answer.

Few movie stars have become quite famous. Charlie Chaplin became famous. Chaplin created a
(36)
distinctive character. The character was known as "the little tramp." The character dressed in
(37)
enormous shoes, baggy pants, and a bowler hat. Chaplain was appearing in silent films. He relied
(38)
on pantomime. He was communicating the tramp's thoughts and feelings. Chaplin was growing up
(39)
in Great Britain. He read comic books. The heroes of these comics were tramplike characters. The
little tramp was based on these characters. Audiences adored the little tramp. Chaplin was helped
(40)
to become famous. He also became wealthy.

36 A Few movie stars have become quite famous, and Charlie Chaplin became famous.
   B Few movie stars have become quite famous, although Charlie Chaplin has become famous.
   C Few movie stars have become quite as famous as Charlie Chaplin.
   D Charlie Chaplin became a famous movie star, and few movie stars became quite famous.

37 F Chaplin created a distinctive character, "the little tramp," who dressed in enormous shoes, baggy pants, and a bowler hat.
   G Chaplin created a character, and the character was distinctive, and he was known as "the little tramp," and he dressed in enormous shoes, baggy pants, and a bowler hat.
   H Chaplin's distinctive character was known as "the little tramp" because he dressed in enormous shoes, baggy pants, and a bowler hat.
   J "The little tramp" created by Chaplin as a character dressed distinctively in enormous shoes, baggy pants, and a bowler hat.

38 A Chaplin appeared in silent films, and he relied on pantomime because he was communicating the tramp's thoughts and feelings.
   B Appearing in silent films, Chaplin relied on pantomime by communicating the tramp's thoughts and feelings.
   C Chaplin relied on pantomime when he was appearing in silent films that was to communicate the tramp's thoughts and feelings.
   D Appearing in silent films, Chaplin relied on pantomime to communicate the tramp's thoughts and feelings.

39 F Chaplin was growing up in Great Britain, and he read comic books, and the heroes of these comics were tramplike characters, and the little tramp was based on these characters.

G When Chaplin was growing up in Great Britain, he read comic books because the heroes of these comics were tramplike characters, so the little tramp was based on these characters.

H When Chaplin was growing up in Great Britain, he read comic books with tramplike characters as heroes, and he based the little tramp on these characters.

J When Chaplin was growing up in Great Britain, he based the little tramp on heroes of comic books who were tramplike characters.

40 A Audiences adored the little tramp because Chaplin became famous and wealthy.

B Audiences adored the little tramp, helping Chaplin to become famous and wealthy.

C Audiences adored the little tramp, and Chaplin became famous, and he became wealthy.

D After audiences adored the little tramp, and Chaplin became famous and wealthy.

Name _____ **Date** _____

 # Assessment for Chapter 20: Effective Sentences

Part 1: Identifying the Four Functions of Sentences

On the line before each sentence, indicate whether the sentence is *declarative, interrogative, imperative,* or *exclamatory.* Then insert the correct end punctuation mark.

1. _____ The invention of the needle changed the way people dressed

2. _____ Are you familiar with clothing in prehistoric times

3. _____ Look at this picture of a prehistoric cave

4. _____ Ivory and bone needles date back thousands of years

5. _____ What amazing discoveries archaeologists have made

Part 2: Combining Sentences

For each item, combine the two sentences by following the direction in parentheses. Write the combined sentence on the lines provided.

6. Elias Howe helped create the sewing machine. So did Isaac Singer. (Use a compound subject.)

   _____

   _____

7. Elias Howe hoped to develop a machine to duplicate his wife's hand-stitching motions. Howe was a Boston merchant. (Use an appositive phrase.)

   _____

   _____

8. That effort failed. Howe devised a new kind of stitch. (Use an adverb clause.)

   _____

   _____

9. Howe's new machine impressed manufacturers. It could produce 250 stitches a minute. (Use an adjective clause.)

   _____

   _____

10. Isaac Singer's machine was produced three years later. It was more versatile and sold for one third the price. (Use a participial phrase.)

   _____

   _____

Part 3: Varying Sentence Beginnings

On the line after each item, rewrite the sentence according to the instructions in parentheses.

11. Judges in China for centuries wore tinted glasses. (Begin with a preposition.)

   _____

12. These early glasses surprisingly did not aim to reduce glare. (Begin with an adverb.)

   _____

13. The judges, hiding their eyes, sought to conceal their reactions during a court case. (Begin with a participle.)

_____

_____

14. True sunglasses came in the twentieth century. (Use inverted order.)

_____

15. Early pilots wore these sunglasses to reduce glare at high altitudes. (Begin with an infinitive.)

_____

Part 4: Revising to Eliminate Fragments and Run-on Sentences

Rewrite the items below to correct any fragments or run-ons. If an item does not need revision. write *correct.*

16. Jonas Hanway was a successful businessman he lived in eighteenth-century England.

_____

_____

17. Made a fortune by trading with Russia and the Far East.

_____

18. Having retired at an early age, Hanway devoted much of his energy to promoting the umbrella.

_____

_____

19. On the streets of London, Hanway always carried an umbrella, it made no difference whether the weather was rainy or fair.

_____

_____

20. Londoners gradually realized that an umbrella was a wise investment. Because of the frequent showers in their city.

_____

_____

Part 5: Identifying and Correcting Misplaced and Dangling Modifiers

On the line after each item, rewrite the item to correct any misplaced or dangling modifiers.

21. The metal can has only been in existence since 1810.

_____

22. As a means of supplying rations to sailors, cans were found to be convenient.

_____

23. Cans before 1820 were brought to America as containers for food preservation.

_____

24. Although virtually ignored for forty years, the Civil War popularized cans.

_____

25. Soldiers needed preserved military rations on both sides.

_____

26. However, early cans were not easy to open for half a century.

   _____

27. Thick-walled and weighing as much as a pound, soldiers used hammers and bayonets to open the cans.

   _____

28. Hoping to improve the situation, the first patented can opener was invented by Ezra J. Warner.

   _____

29. To access the can's contents, the opener's blade must be moved carefully around the rim.

   _____

30. Although unpopular with the public, the military used Warner's can opener.

   _____

Part 6: Revising to Eliminate Faulty Parallelism
On the line after each sentence, rewrite the sentence to correct nonparallel structure.

31. Chess, checkers, and the game of backgammon have been popular since ancient times.

   _____

32. In ancient Egypt, a game called senet was played by peasants, artisans, and those who ruled.

   _____

33. Each senet player moved ivory pieces or pieces made out of stone across a papyrus playing board.

   _____

34. Historians argue over whether chess was invented in India or by the Persians.

   _____

35. Thousands of years ago, people enjoyed playing games, running races, and to wrestle.

   _____

Part 7: Correcting Faulty Coordination
On the line after each sentence, rewrite the sentence to correct the faulty coordination.

36. For centuries people had only simple means of washing their clothes, and on sea voyages they would put their laundry in a bag and let the ship drag it in the water.

   _____

   _____

37. The first hand-operated washing machines used a "dolly," and this device fitted into a tub and pummeled the clothes.

   _____

   _____

38. Many odd inventions were devised to wash clothes, and it is generally agreed that actual washing machines first appeared in the early 1800's.

   _____

   _____

39. The earliest washing machines were wooden boxes, and the user tumbled the box by using a hand crank.

_____

_____

40. Mothers and daughters took turns, and they cranked the box's handle.

_____

Part 8: Standardized Test Practice

Directions: Read the following passage. Then, answer the questions below the passage by circling the letter of the best answer.

[1]Today many people are singing the praises of electronic mail. [2]Electronic mail is fast, cheap, and easy to send. [3]You can attach pictures and sounds to an e-mail message. [4]You can also attach videos and other binary files to an e-mail message. [5]You can send a single message to a large group of people using a mailing list. [6]E-mail has the advantage of being fast. [7]It may also encourage sloppy writing, as some experts feel. [8]Tend to be less thoughtful about correct grammar, spelling, and punctuation.

41. Which of the following is the best way to combine sentences 1 and 2?
   A. Fast, cheap, and easy to send; electronic mail is the subject of many people's praises today.
   B. Today many people are singing the praises of electronic mail, which is fast, cheap, and easy to send.
   C. Today many people are singing the praises of electronic mail, and it is fast, cheap, and easy to send.
   D. Electronic mail, that is fast and cheap and easy to send, is sung about in many people's praises today.

42. Which of the following is the best way to combine sentences 3 and 4?
   A. You can attach pictures and sounds to an e-mail message, and you can also attach videos and other binary files to an e-mail message.
   B. To an e-mail message you can attach pictures and sounds; to it can also be attached videos and other binary files.
   C. In addition to pictures and sounds, videos and binary files can also be attached by you to an e-mail message.
   D. You can attach pictures, sounds, videos, and other binary files to an e-mail message.

43. Which of the following is the best way to rewrite sentence 5?
   A. Using a mailing list, you can send a single message to a large group of people.
   B. You can send a single message, using a mailing list, to a large group of people.
   C. A large group of people can be sent a single message, using a mailing list.
   D. Because you use a mailing list, you can send a single message to a large group of people.

44. Which of the following is the best way to combine sentences 6 and 7?
   A. As some experts feel, e-mail has the advantage of being fast, and it may also encourage sloppy writing.
   B. E-mail has the advantage of being fast; it may also encourage sloppy writing, as some experts feel.
   C. Although e-mail has the advantage of being fast, some experts feel that it may encourage sloppy writing.
   D. E-mail has the advantage of being fast, it may also encourage sloppy writing, some experts feel.

45. Which of the following is the best way to rewrite sentence 8?
   A. E-mail writers tend to be less thoughtful about correct grammar, spelling, and punctuation.
   B. E-mail writers tend to be less thoughtful. About correct grammar, spelling, and punctuation.
   C. Tending to be less thoughtful, e-mail writers need to correct grammar, spelling, and punctuation.
   D. E-mail writers tend to be less thoughtful, they often neglect correct grammar, spelling, and punctuation.

㉑ Assessment for Chapter 21: Verb Usage

Part 1: Identifying Verb Tenses and Forms

On the line after each sentence, identify the tense of the italicized verb and tell whether the form is *basic*, *progressive*, or *emphatic*.

1. Gardening *has been gaining* popularity as a hobby. _____

2. Gary *did plant* those roses last year. _____

3. These tomatoes *will have ripened* by the end of August. _____

4. Perennials *are* plants that live more than two years. _____

5. By noon, Joanne *had planted* more than a dozen bushes. _____

Part 2: Forming Tenses of Verbs

On the lines provided, write the listed verbs in the tenses indicated, with the pronouns in parentheses as their subjects.

6. past perfect of *grow* (it) _____

7. present emphatic of *prepare* (I) _____

8. future perfect of *sell* (they) _____

9. past progressive of *dig* (we) _____

10. past emphatic of *draw* (you) _____

Part 3: Using Irregular Verbs

On the line after each sentence, write the form of the verb that correctly completes each sentence.

11. Last year, Silas (strive) to plant a flower garden. _____

12. The garden (grow) nicely in the first few weeks. _____

13. Then one morning a big problem (arise). _____

14. A late winter storm had (strike) the garden in the night. _____

15. The wind had (blow) some of the taller plants down. _____

16. Several of the plants (lie) on their sides. _____

17. One plant had (shrink) to half its normal size. _____

18. Luckily, the ground had not (freeze). _____

19. The sunlight (bring) many of the plants back to life. _____

20. Silas (fight) all day to save his garden. _____

Part 4: Supplying Correct Verb Tenses

On the line provided, supply the form of the verb in parentheses that will correctly complete each sentence.

21. Until fairly recent times, few homes (have) lawns. _____

22. Those homeowners who did grow grass usually (keep) it untidy. _____

23. By the time American novelist Nathaniel Hawthorne visited England in the 1850's, solid-green lawns (become) fasionable there. _____

24. Dismayed by what he (see), Hawthorne criticized British lawns as artificial. _____

25. Until the lawn mower (be) invented, flocks of sheep often trimmed the grass. _____

26. By the 1820's, however, English textile worker Edward Budding already (begin) experiments with a

rotary shearing machine. _____

27. Edwin George (produce) the first gasoline-powered lawn mower in 1919. _____

28. Around the same time, a weed-free grass seed (appear) on the market. _____

29. Weed-free grass seed and the mower have contributed to the lawns people (enjoy) today. _____

30. However, it is uncertain whether lawns (receive) the same attention in years to come.

_____

Part 5: Using the Subjunctive Mood

On the line after each sentence, write the correct form of the underlined verb. If the verb is correct as is, write *correct*.

31. If Justin was to have a garden, he would like to grow roses. _____

32. Maria insists that her workers be careful with lawn chemicals. _____

33. It is required that each user studies the label carefully. _____

34. Sam proposed that detailed plans are prepared for fall pruning. _____

35. It is suggested that one checks the forecast before planting. _____

Part 6: Distinguishing Between Active and Passive Voice

Underline the verb in each sentence. Then, identify whether the verb is active or passive.

36. Some plants are better started indoors. _____

37. A controlled environment aids seed germination. _____

38. Heat-sensitive vegetables will reach maturity before midsummer. _____

39. Seedling growth might have been improved by better light. _____

40. The public gardens in our city have been much admired. _____

Part 7: Standardized Test Practice

Directions: Read the passage, and choose the letter of the word or group of words that belongs in each space

By late July last summer we _____(41)_____ no rain for six weeks.

On nine days during that period, temperatures _____(42)_____ to record highs. All over town, the

grass _____(43)_____ brown, and people's flowers and vegetables were desperate for water.

"If the drought continues," said Elena, "those tomato vines _____(44)_____ and die."

"I just heard some good news on the radio," said Jess. "The long-range forecast predicts that the

drought _____(45)_____ by the start of next week."

41 A are seeing B saw C have seen D had seen	**43** A is turning B was turning C will have been turning D has turned	**45** A has broken B breaks C had broken D will have broken
42 F climb G are climbing H will climb J climbed	**44** F are withering G did wither H will wither J will have withered	

Assessment for Chapter 22: Pronoun Usage

Part 1: Identifying Case

Circle the pronoun in each item. Then, identify its case as *nominative*, *objective*, or *possessive*.

1. their tools _____

2. gave her the hammer _____

3. my brush _____

4. we started work _____

5. its roof _____

6. was repaired by us _____

7. saw you in the workshop _____

8. the best worker was she _____

9. lunch for me _____

10. I painted the wall _____

Part 2: Using Pronouns Correctly

Circle the pronoun in parentheses that correctly completes each sentence. Then, on the line provided, write whether the pronoun is used as a *subject*, as a *predicate nominative*, as a *nominative absolute*, as a *direct object*, as an *indirect object*, as the *object of a preposition*, as the *object of a verbal*, as the *subject of an infinitive*, or to show *ownership*.

11. Mr. Santoro sold Randy and (we, us) a tool kit. _____

12. Randy and (I, me) are learning to repair appliances. _____

13. Randy fixed the light when (its, it's) switch broke. _____

14. (We, Us) students will use power tools for that job. _____

15. The best painter in our group is (she, her). _____

16. Expenses for one project were paid by Stacy and (they, them). _____

17. People could hear (their, them) hammering a block away. _____

18. Dad has taken on the task of teaching (we, us) hand lettering. _____

19. (Their, They're) signs are not as nicely painted. _____

20. The best sign painters are (we, us) students. _____

Part 3: Using Pronouns in the Nominative Case

Write a nominative pronoun to complete each sentence. Then, on the line after the sentence, write whether the pronoun is used as a *subject*, a *predicate nominative*, or a *nominative absolute*.

21. My friends and _____ are partners in a company. _____

22. _____ partners offer home-repair services in the neighborhood. _____

23. The best roofers in the group are Marcus, Tanya, and _____. _____

24. It was _____ who designed our advertisements. _____

25. _____ having bid for that project, our competitors looked elsewhere. _____

Part 4: Using Pronouns in the Objective Case

Write an objective pronoun to complete each sentence. Then, on the line after the sentence, write whether the pronoun is a *direct object*, an *indirect object*, an *object of a preposition*, an *object of a participle*, an *object of a gerund*, an *object of an infinitive*, or a *subject of an infinitive*.

26. Between you and _____, cleaning a house is hard work. _____

27. The customers wanted Ben and _____ to wash the windows. _____

28. The vacuum broke, causing _____ some problems. _____

29. Working with Lisa, I helped _____ with the ironing. _____

30. Mr. Lane brought _____ thirsty workers some cold drinks. _____

Part 5: Using *Who* and *Whom* Correctly

Circle the pronoun in parentheses that correctly completes each sentence. Then, on the line provided, write whether the pronoun is used as a *subject*, as a *predicate nominative*, as a *direct object*, as an *indirect object*, as the *object of a preposition*, as the *object of a verbal*, or to show *ownership*.

31. (Who, Whom), may I ask, will dust the blinds? _____

32. (Who, Whom) are we meeting this afternoon? _____

33. Do you know (who, whom) has asked for our help? _____

34. From (who, whom) did you get a contract in the mail? _____

35. (Whose, Who's) roof needs repair? _____

Part 6: Using the Correct Pronoun in Elliptical Clauses

For each item, circle the pronoun in parentheses that correctly completes the elliptical clause.

36. Rona studied the parts manual more carefully than (I, me).

37. Doing a thorough job is a higher priority for us than (they, them).

38. Mr. and Mrs. Torres paid Gary more than (I, me).

39. Rebecca can work as fast as (I, me).

40. The truth is that Art cleans as well as (we, us).

Part 7: Standardized Test Practice

Directions: Read the passage, and choose the letter of the word or group of words that belongs in each space.

_____(41)_____ fixing the roof was a top priority. The workers assigned to the task were Terry,

Sandy, and _____(42)_____. Terry completed nailing in his portion of the shingles more quickly than

_____(43)_____. Paul called Sandy and asked _____(44)_____ to help us clear any debris left behind. Paul

wanted _____(45)_____ workers to finish by dusk, and we did.

41 A We	**43 A** I	**45 A** we
B Us	**B** me	**B** their
C Our	**C** my	**C** ours
D Ours	**D** mine	**D** us
42 F I	**44 F** she	
G me	**G** her	
H my	**H** hers	
J mine	**J** they	

Assessment for Chapter 23: Agreement

Part 1: Making Subjects and Verbs Agree
Complete each sentence by circling the verb in parentheses that agrees with its subject.

1. The adventures of Coyote (is, are) among the most popular Native American tales.

2. Trickery and scheming (is, are) Coyote's specialties.

3. Coyote's cleverness, together with his foolishness, (makes, make) him a distinctive character.

4. A number of myths (features, feature) Coyote as a cultural hero.

5. Lynx is only one of several animals who (is, are) Coyote's companions.

6. "Coyote, Iktome, and the Rock" (is, are) a Sioux story about Coyote.

7. The Sioux (has, have) told this tale to their children for generations.

8. Craftiness that alternates with foolishness (seems, seem) to prompt Coyote's behavior.

9. Neither the stars nor the moon (is, are) immune from his thievery.

10. Ethics (does, do) not generally motivate a trickster like Coyote.

11. Nevertheless, Coyote is sometimes outsmarted by those he (tries, try) to trick.

12. In the body of tales (is, are) important lessons on human behavior.

13. Everyone usually (listens, listen) intently when the Coyote tales are read aloud.

14. Every twist and turn of the plot (brings, bring) chuckles.

15. Only about half of the tales (is, are) included in this anthology.

Part 2: Making Pronouns and Antecedents Agree
Circle the appropriate personal pronoun in parentheses to complete each sentence.

16. Either Tom or Al will present (his, their) report on Tlingit legends.

17. Everyone will then have a chance to ask (his or her, their) questions.

18. Students in the class should then read the legends (himself, themselves).

19. If your sisters or Roberto wants to reread the legend beforehand, encourage (him, them) to do so.

20. The Tlingit people of the Northwest center many of (its, their) myths around the character of Raven.

21. Raven, like Prometheus of Greek mythology, is a bringer of fire to (his, their) people.

22. Neither Coyote nor Raven is without (his, their) sneaky side.

23. Raven employs trickery because (he, you) can often get the upper hand by fooling others.

24. According to the myths, all of the world's freshwater rivers and lakes owe (its, their) creation to Raven.

25. An actual raven is a large bird whose black coat gives it a startling appearance and makes (him, it) seem gloomy.

26. Most of the world's mythology has trickster characters in (it, them).

27. Anansi the Spider, who resembles both Coyote and Raven to a certain degree, makes (his, their) appearance in many African tales.

28. When the students meet again, (he or she, they) will learn more about Anansi.

29. Someone is scheduled to give (his or her, their) report about the trickster spider.

30. Both Alice and Joyce will have (her, their) work on Mexican mythology ready then, too.

Part 3: Revising to Correct Vague, Ambiguous, or Distant Pronoun References

On the lines provided, rewrite the following sentences, correcting the vague, ambiguous, or distant pronoun references

31. Tall tales are humorous, exaggerated stories that you tell as if they were fact.

_____

_____

32. When Maria told Denise some tall tales about Pecos Bill, she could not stop laughing.

_____

_____

33. In the Old West, passengers on stagecoach rides swapped tall tales. They made the time go by faster.

_____

34. Both Mike Fink and Davy Crockett were real frontiersmen whose adventures were exaggerated in the retelling. They were very popular.

_____

_____

35. In the 1800's, Crockett was such a popular figure that you heard his story everywhere.

_____

_____

36. Crockett was an adventurer, cowboy, war hero, and Congressman. Even without exaggeration, it was pretty amazing.

_____

_____

37. Like Davy Crockett, Daniel Boone was a real-life frontiersman whose life became legendary. This makes the stories more interesting.

_____

_____

38. Paul Bunyan and Pecos Bill lived only in folk tales. Folk tales are popular in many countries. They both had outrageous exploits.

_____

_____

39. Paul Bunyan and his blue ox, Babe, roamed the northern forests. They were the perfect setting for stories about a giant lumberjack.

_____

_____

40. New tall tales continue to appear; you often hear them in the routines of stand-up comics.

_____

_____

Name _____

Part 4: Standardized Test Practice

Directions: In the following sentences, circle the letter of the underlined word or phrase that contains an error.

41. In the folklore <u>of many cultures</u> <u>are tales of characters</u> <u>who plays tricks</u> on <u>others</u>. <u>No error</u>.
              (A)   (B)   (C)   (D) (E)

42. The trickster, <u>together with other characters</u>, <u>convey a message</u> about human behavior <u>to an</u>
              (A)   (B)   (C)

     <u>audience that laughs</u> <u>at the unlikely events</u>. <u>No error</u>.
                  (D)   (E)

43. <u>The trickster in many of the tales</u> <u>takes animal form</u>. For example, <u>he or she may be a coyote, a</u>
    (A)   (B)   (C)

     <u>raven, or a spider</u>. <u>It will always be an animal with which listeners are familiar</u>. <u>No error</u>.
                  (D)   (E)

44. <u>Each of the ancient Greek gods</u> <u>usually plays</u> <u>their tricks</u> on unsuspecting humans, <u>who rarely</u>
    (A)   (B)   (C)   (D)

     <u>triumph</u>. <u>No error</u>.
              (E)

45. <u>Either those myths or that legend</u> <u>is notable</u> <u>for clever twists and turns</u> <u>in their plots</u>. <u>No error</u>.
    (A)   (B)   (C)   (D)   (E)

24 Assessment for Chapter 24: Using Modifiers

Part 1: Forming Comparative and Superlative Degrees
On the lines provided, write the comparative and superlative degrees of these modifiers.

1. pretty _____ _____

2. sympathetic _____ _____

3. wisely _____ _____

4. ill _____ _____

5. majestic _____ _____

6. badly _____ _____

7. lovely _____ _____

8. gracefully _____ _____

9. fast _____ _____

10. rapid _____ _____

11. far _____ _____

12. well _____ _____

13. costly _____ _____

14. foolish _____ _____

15. odd _____ _____

Part 2: Identifying Degrees of Comparison
On the line after each sentence, identify the degree of the underlined modifier as *positive, comparative,* or *superlative.*

16. Few accessories are <u>more useful</u> than a wristwatch. _____

17. The wristwatch is a <u>comparatively</u> recent invention, however. _____

18. Until the late 1800's, <u>most</u> people carried pocket watches. _____

19. Of course, a wristwatch is <u>less cumbersome</u> than a pocket watch. _____

20. In 1904, an aviator wore one of the <u>earliest</u> wristwatches. _____

Part 3: Using Comparative and Superlative Degrees Correctly
Complete each sentence by circling the correct modifier in parentheses.

21. As watchmaking improved, parts became (smaller, more smaller) and wristwatches became possible.

22. Compared with pocket watches, wristwatches proved (more, most) popular.

23. Because of the wristwatch, other machinery became (tinier, tiniest) than ever before.

24. People wondered how the miniaturization of machinery could progress any (more far, further).

25. Of self-winding and tuning-fork watches, which was the (less, least) recent invention?

26. Self-winding watches appeared (earlier, more earlier) than you might have imagined.

27. In the 1960's, tuning-fork watches were the (later, latest) high-tech watch variety.

28. At the New York World's Fair in 1964, these watches were hailed as some of the (best, most best) examples of technological innovation.

29. Compared with tuning-fork watches, quartz watches are the (more, most) sophisticated.

30. Which of the two watches is (costlier, costliest)?

Part 4: Revising for Logical Comparisons and Absolute Modifiers

On the lines provided, rewrite the following sentences to make the comparisons logical or to correct use of absolute modifiers. If the sentence is correct as is, write *correct*.

31. The art of watchmaking is most unique.

_____

32. For generations of watchmakers, overcoming friction was more important than anything.

_____

_____

33. Are Swiss watches made better than any watch?

_____

34. Watchmaking in Japan is almost as good as Switzerland.

_____

35. My Japanese watch is better than any watch I've ever owned.

_____

36. No two watches are more identical than the two Jan owns.

_____

37. Is the accuracy of a clock better than a watch?

_____

38. I like an older clock with a pendulum better than any kind of clock.

_____

39. In winter, a clock's pendulum swings faster than summer.

_____

40. Do atomic clocks keep more perfect time than other clocks do?

_____

Part 5: Standardized Test Practice

Directions: Read the passage, and choose the letter of the word or group of words that belongs in each space.

No clocks have changed ____(41)____ over time than pendulum clocks. The pendulum clocks that we use today are ____(42)____ to earlier models than are any other types of clocks. Of all pendulum clocks, the ____(43)____ were built by a Dutch scientist named Christiaan Huygens in the 1650's. Huygens had many creative ideas, but his decision to use a pendulum in a clock was the ____(44)____. Huygens's new clocks were more accurate than ____(45)____ clocks of their time. His pendulum clocks were also ____(46)____ than earlier clocks. The secret to Huygens's clock was establishing the ____(47)____ length for the pendulum. By lengthening the pendulum, Huygens could make it go ____(48)____. If he made it too long, however, the pendulum would run ____(49)____ than necessary. In the 1650's, Europeans who wanted accurate clocks had to go no ____(50)____ than Holland to find them.

41 A little
   B littler
   C least
   D less

42 F more identical
   G identical
   H more similar
   J similar

43 A most famous
   B famousest
   C famouser
   D more famous

44 F successful
   G successfulest
   H more successful
   J most successful

45 A any
   B those
   C any other
   D all of the

46 F less bulky
   G least bulky
   H less bulkier
   J least bulkiest

47 A most exact
   B more exact
   C exact
   D exactest

48 F slowlier
   G slowliest
   H more slowly
   J most slowliest

49 A slow
   B most slowly
   C more slowly
   D slowest

50 F farther
   G further
   H farthest
   J more farther

Assessment for Chapter 25:
Miscellaneous Problems in Usage

Part 1: Revising Sentences to Avoid Double Negatives
On the lines provided, rewrite each of these sentences to eliminate problems with negatives. If the sentence is correct as is, write *correct*.

1. Before last summer, we hadn't never been to Washington, D.C.

   _____

2. There probably isn't no other city more interesting to visit.

   _____

3. You don't have no idea how impressive the monuments are!

   _____

4. We didn't barely have time to see all the tourist attractions.

   _____

5. We hadn't but a long weekend to spend in Washington.

   _____

6. We couldn't spend scarcely an hour at the Lincoln Memorial.

   _____

7. There wasn't no one who wanted to miss the White House.

   _____

8. Hardly none of the sites we visited charged admission.

   _____

9. Didn't nobody use a camera during the trip?

   _____

10. We weren't able to take pictures because we didn't have enough time.

    _____

Part 2: Revising Sentences to Use Understatement
On the lines provided, rewrite each sentence so that it achieves understatement by using a negative word and a word with a negative prefix.

11. A visit to the Washington Monument is interesting.

    _____

12. The sight of the Capitol dome is inspiring.

    _____

13. Most visitors to Washington are happy with their experience.

    _____

14. Visitors find that the city is exciting.

    _____

15. The floodlighting of many public buildings at night is attractive.

    _____

Part 3: Avoiding Usage Problems
Circle the word or expression that correctly completes each sentence.

16. We spent (awhile, a while) at the Smithsonian's many museums.

17. After visiting the National Air and Space Museum, we (preceded, proceeded) down Constitution Avenue.

18. (Being that, Because) it was so hot and humid, we walked slowly.

19. We stood (outside, outside of) the National Gallery of Art to admire the architecture of the East Wing.

20. Since no one (can, may) bring packages inside the museum, Adam had to check his briefcase in the cloakroom.

21. The National Gallery has (a, an) unique collection of American art.

22. Do you ever (loose, lose) your way in a big museum?

23. Stuart liked the Dutch paintings more (than, then) the Italian ones.

24. (Everyone, Every one) of Vermeer's paintings is a masterpiece.

25. Ali and I respect (each other's, one another's) opinions of modern art.

26. We saw (fewer, less) really modern pieces than we had expected.

27. We had no time to go (in, into) the Hirschhorn Gallery.

28. (Beside, Besides) Winslow Homer's works, what other American paintings did you admire?

29. Mona was (anxious, eager) to see the John Singer Sargent exhibit.

30. By the time we arrived in Washington, however, that exhibit had (gone, went) to the Museum of Fine Arts in Boston.

Part 4: Chapter Review
On the lines provided, revise these sentences, eliminating any usage errors or mistakes in negative sentences. If there are no errors, write *correct*.

31. The Statue of Liberty is one of New York's principle tourist attractions.

_____

32. One reason the statue is popular is because it is a symbol of freedom.

_____

33. Before our visit there, I never knew nothing about the monument.

_____

34. From history books, I should of known it was a gift from France.

_____

35. The organization who gave us the statue was the Franco-American Union.

_____

36. Liberty Island, where the statue stands, lays in Upper New York Bay.

_____

37. Visitors making there way to the crown must climb no less than 354 steps.

_____

38. Besides visiting the statue, people also tour Ellis Island nearby.

_____

39. Hardly no immigrant entry point used to be busier than Ellis Island.

_____

40. We toured the Ellis Island museum altogether but split up outside.

_____

Part 5: Standardized Test Practice

Directions: After reading this passage, answer the questions below it by circling the letter of the correct answer. The questions refer to the numbered sentences in the passage.

[1]Hardly no relics are more famous than the Liberty Bell, which sits outside Independence Hall in Philadelphia. [2]Patriotic citizens proceeded to ring the bell for awhile when the Declaration of Independence was adopted in July 1776. [3]Being that the bell is associated with the principle of liberty, the biblical quotation that appears on the bell reads, "Proclaim Liberty throughout all the Land." [4]As you might have guessed, the bell was kind of controversial when British troops occupied Philadelphia during the Revolution. [5]Except for those years, the ringing of the Liberty Bell was an Independence Day tradition for seventy years. [6]In 1846, however, the bell could be rung no further, for its famous crack had become too large to allow the bell to be rung safely.

41. Which of these changes is needed in Sentence 1?
    A. Change *no* to *any*.
    B. Change *than* to *then*.
    C. Add *of* after *outside*.
    D. No changes are necessary.

42. Which of these changes is needed in Sentence 2?
    A. Change *proceeded* to *preceded*.
    B. Make *awhile* two words.
    C. Change *adopted* to *adapted*.
    D. No changes are necessary.

43. Which of these changes is needed in Sentence 3?
    A. Change *Being that* to *Because*.
    B. Change *principle* to *principal*.
    C. Change the second *that* to *who*.
    D. No changes are necessary.

44. Which of these changes is needed in Sentences 4 and 5?
    A. Change *have* to *of*.
    B. Change *kind of* to *rather*.
    C. Change *Except* to *Accept*.
    D. No changes are necessary.

45. Which of these changes is needed in Sentence 6?
    A. Change *no* to *any*.
    B. Change *further* to *farther*.
    C. Change *too* to *two*.
    D. No changes are necessary.

26 Assessment for Chapter 26: Capitalization

Part 1: Using Capitals for First Words

For each item, circle the letter or letters that should be capitalized.

1. "oh! marvelous! we are going on vacation at last," said Melly.

2. "where are you going," Jo asked, "and when do you leave?"

3. "my family leaves for New England next week," said Melly. "we are stopping at a farm that was once owned by Robert Frost."

4. Robert Frost did more than just write poetry: he was a college professor for many years.

5. Frost once wrote, "something there is that doesn't love a wall."

Part 2: Capitalizing Proper Nouns and Proper Adjectives

On the line after each item, correctly rewrite any word or words that should start with capital letters and indicate whether each word is a *proper noun* or a *proper adjective*.

6. the hungarian language _____

7. the state of missouri _____

8. a july day _____

9. a swedish-speaking singer _____

10. senator barbara boxer _____

11. the easter holiday this spring _____

12. laurel o'boyle, m.d. _____

13. I loved the book *lad, a dog* _____

14. american dream _____

15. elm and oak streets _____

Part 3: Proofreading for Correct Capitalization

For each item, circle the letters that should be capitalized.

16. straddling the north carolina-tennessee border, great smoky mountains national park was authorized by congress in 1926.

17. with about ten million visitors a year, this park is one of the most popular in the united states.

18. the park contains part of the appalachian trail, which extends all the way from mt. katahdin in maine to springer mountain in georgia.

19. last week, governor ann e. brady met with several members of the sierra club at the park.

20. within the park are 130 native trees, more than in all of europe.

21. yosemite national park is one of the most popular parks in the west.

22. it is located in the sierra nevada, a mountain range in central california.

23. my cousin carla will visit the park this autumn with her peruvian pen pal, who is staying with carla for three weeks.

24. they will head west next thursday, thanksgiving day, and will be on the west coast for the rest of november.

25. carla, a long-time member of the girl scouts, just bought a zipomatic backpack and a swiss army knife for camping out.

Part 4: Using Capitals Correctly in Letters

The items in this exercise are different sections of a friendly letter. Rewrite each section on the lines provided, correcting any errors in capitalization.

26. 2620 north magnolia street _____

    chicago, illinois 60614 _____

27. june 1, 20– _____

28. mrs. thelma ryan _____

    2314 carol view drive _____

    cardiff, california 92007 _____

29. my dear aunt thelma, _____

30. very truly yours, _____

Part 5: Correcting Errors in Capitalization

On the lines after each sentence, correctly rewrite the sentence, adding or eliminating capital letters as needed.

31. For american citizens, elections are held the first tuesday after the first monday in november.

    _____

    _____

32. every four years, the president of the united states is inaugurated on january 20 at noon.

    _____

    _____

33. Before the twentieth amendment to the constitution was ratified in 1933, however, the president was inaugurated in early march.

    _____

    _____

34. My Uncle, louis d. pezza, jr., always celebrates the fourth of july with a cookout at his home on park and main streets.

    _____

    _____

35. Memorial day, formerly called decoration day, was first observed in 1868 to honor the civil war dead.

    _____

    _____

36. Did you know that labor day, which falls on the First Monday in september, is celebrated in both the u.s. and canada?

    _____

    _____

37. In late november, thanksgiving day recalls the Harvest of the pilgrim settlers at plymouth colony in 1621.

    _____

    _____

38. The new york symphony orchestra will celebrate new year's day with a special Concert at lincoln center.

_____

_____

39. Will Ex-senator Gordon be appointed President of duke university, one of the finest universities in the south?

_____

_____

40. I asked grandmother and aunt nelly if they would come east to visit us around mother's day.

_____

_____

Part 6: Standardized Test Practice

Directions: On the line before each number, write the letter of the underlined word or phrase that contains an error in capitalization. If a sentence has no error in capitalization, choose D ("No error").

_____ 41. On July 1, our neighbors to the North celebrate Canada Day. No error.
              (A)   (B)   (C)   (D)

_____ 42. The holiday commemorates the British North America Act of 1867, which united several
                                    (A)

provinces in an early step toward canadian independence. No error.
(B)   (C)   (D)

_____ 43. The celebrations resemble Fourth of July festivities: My relatives in Ontario attend picnics
                               (A)   (B)   (C)

and parades. No error.
          (D)

_____ 44. My Cousin Dr. Jean Andrews speaks French and English fluently. No error.
      (A)   (B)   (C)   (D)

_____ 45. "When I come to visit," my cousin told me, "let's go to the mall at Robin and Quail streets
                                         (A)   (B)

and buy a pair of Blue Moon Blue Jeans." No error.
               (C)   (D)

Assessment for Chapter 27: Punctuation

Part 1: Supplying Correct End Marks
Add the appropriate end marks to these sentences.

1. Madagascar is the fourth-largest island in the world

2. Is it located off the coast of Africa

3. Wow The orchids are magnificent

4. I asked Dr. Richardson which city is the capital

5. The documentary film about Madagascar begins at 2 P.M

Part 2: Proofreading Sentences for Commas
Insert commas where they are needed in these sentences. Circle the commas you add.

6. Separated from East Africa by the Mozambique Channel Madagascar lies in the Indian Ocean.

7. The country's economy is mainly agricultural and the most important crops are rice coffee vanilla and sugar cane.

8. Natural resources which include many minerals also contribute to the island's economy.

9. According to historians Africans and Indonesians first reached Madagascar about 2000 years ago.

10. Arriving in 1500 the first Europeans to visit the island were the Portuguese.

Part 3: Proofreading Sentences for Semicolons and Colons
Insert *semicolons* and *colons* where they are needed in these sentences. Circle the punctuation marks you add.

11. In the past, Madagascar was heavily forested today, however, many of the island's forests have disappeared.

12. Madagascar possesses a unique treasure biodiversity.

13. Many of the island's plants and animals are "endemic" They can be found nowhere else in the world.

14. Endangered animals in Madagascar include the following chameleons, radiated tortoises, and many species of lemur.

15. Most lemur species are arboreal in fact, they seldom descend to the ground.

Part 4: Supplying Quotation Marks and Underlining
Insert *quotation marks* and *underlining* where they are needed in these sentences.

16. If you are interested in lemurs, said Mr. Sanders, you may want to consult some reference books in the library.

17. An excellent book on the island's fauna is Mammals of Madagascar by Nick Garbutt, he continued.

18. Mr. Sanders told us that the author included a useful chapter called Conservation and Protected Areas.

19. Recently, I read a magazine article in Time entitled A Global Green Deal.

20. Is that the article in which the author says, We have in hand most of the technologies needed to chart a new course?

Part 5: Supplying Dashes, Parentheses, and Brackets

Insert *dashes*, *parentheses*, and *brackets* where they are needed in these sentences. Words inserted into a quotation by another person are underlined in the sentences.

21. So far, scientists have identified numerous species about 1.75 million but this may be only the beginning.

22. The total number of species as we learned at the Museum of Natural History may be as great as 100 million.

23. Tropical rain forests you may be amazed to discover are thought to contain more than half the species on earth.

24. According to an article I read recently, "It biodiversity is a complex web of plant and animal species."

25. Gifford Pinchot 1865–1946 was one of President Theodore Roosevelt's strongest allies in support of conservation.

Part 6: Using Hyphens to Join Words

On the lines provided, rewrite the following items, adding *hyphens* where they are needed. If an item needs no hyphens added. write *correct*.

26. prehistoric times _____

27. widely distributed species _____

28. up to date statistics _____

29. third largest island _____

30. self possessed exgovernor _____

31. sociable mothers in law _____

32. mid March madness _____

33. ten minute free for all _____

34. five year old child _____

35. German born biologist _____

Part 7: Using Apostrophes

On the lines provided, rewrite the items below, following the instructions in parentheses.

36. the medicinal plants of the rain forest (Use the possessive case.)

_____

37. could not (Write the contraction of these two words.)

_____

38. they are (Write the contraction of these two words.)

_____

39. the borders of India and Nepal (Use the possessive case.)

_____

40. the sound of it (Use the possessive case.)

_____

Part 8: Standardized Test Practice

Directions: In the questions below the marked passage, circle the letter of the choice that shows the best way to write each underlined section. If the underlined section needs no change, choose *D*.

"Endangered species in India" Ms. Varma told us "include the tiger the Asian elephant and the
(41)

Indian one-horned rhinoceros."

Amy then wanted to know how many tigers are still in the wild.
(42)

"Because tigers are secretive and largely nocturnal. Ms. Varma explained, it is hard to know
(43)

exactly". Ms. Varma continued. "Scientists now estimate that there are no more than 5,000 tigers in
(44)

the wild more than half of these are believed to live in India."

Chuck, a self described animal lover, asked about the tiger and its future in the animal kingdom's
(45)

energy pyramid, and he listened intently for Ms Varmas reply.

41 A "Endangered species in India", Ms. Varma told us, "include the tiger, the Asian elephant and the Indian one-horned rhinoceros."
　B "Endangered species in India" Ms. Varma told us "include the tiger, the Asian elephant, and the Indian one-horned rhinoceros.
　C "Endangered species in India," Ms. Varma told us. "include the tiger, the Asian elephant, and the Indian one-horned rhinoceros."
　D Correct as is

42 F Amy then wanted to know "How many tigers are still in the wild."
　G Amy then wanted to know how many tigers are still in the wild?
　H Amy then wanted to know, how many tigers are still in the wild.
　J Correct as is

43 A "Because tigers are secretive and largely nocturnal," Ms. Varma explained, "it is hard to know exactly."
　B "Because tigers are secretive and largely nocturnal", Ms. Varma explained, "it is hard to know exactly."
　C "Because tigers are secretive and largely nocturnal," Ms. Varma explained, "It is hard to know exactly."
　D Correct as is

44 F Ms. Varma continued; "Scientists now estimate that there are no more than 5,000 tigers in the wild and more than half of these are believed to live in India."
　G Ms. Varma continued, "Scientists now estimate that there are no more than 5,000 tigers in the wild; more than half of these are believed to live in India."
　H Ms. Varma continued: "Scientists now estimate that: there are no more than 5000 tigers in the wild, more than half of these are believed to live in India."
　J Correct as is

45 A Chuck, a self-described animal lover, asked about the tiger and it's future in the animal kingdom's energy pyramid, and he listened intently for Ms. Varmas reply.
　B Chuck, a self described animal-lover, asked about the tiger and its future in the animal kingdom's energy pyramid, and he listened intently for Ms. Varmas reply.
　C Chuck, a self-described animal lover, asked about the tiger and its future in the animal kingdom's energy pyramid, and he listened intently for Ms. Varma's reply.
　D Correct as is

Grammar, Usage, and Mechanics: Cumulative Mastery Test

Part 1: Identifying Parts of Speech
On the line after each sentence, identify the part of speech of each underlined word or group of words.

1. Born in 1758 <u>in</u> West Hartford, Connecticut, <u>Noah Webster</u> graduated from Yale and <u>fought</u> in the American Revolution.

   _____

2. After returning <u>home</u>, Webster started <u>out</u> as a lawyer.

   _____

3. <u>While</u> he was still in his <u>twenties</u>, Webster began to write books.

   _____

4. His first <u>three</u> volumes—a speller, a grammar, and a <u>reader</u>—were <u>highly</u> successful.

   _____

5. A <u>smash</u> hit on the market, Webster's speller sold more than eighty million copies <u>during</u> the author's lifetime.

   _____

6. These <u>sales</u> made the book <u>second</u> in popularity <u>only</u> to the Bible.

   _____

7. The <u>sales</u> force, in fact, offered both books <u>together</u> in a <u>package</u> deal.

   _____

8. <u>Frontier</u> children learned to read from Webster's *Elementary Spelling Book*, <u>which</u> was a basic school text.

   _____

9. Webster successfully <u>backed</u> the <u>passage</u> of a national copyright law in <u>1790</u>.

   _____

10. <u>Aha</u>! <u>Here</u> is an <u>unabridged</u> edition of Webster's *American Dictionary of the English Language*.

   _____

Part 2: Identifying Parts of a Sentence
Follow the directions in parentheses at the end of each sentence.

11. Decorating a house is tricky but also fulfilling. (Underline the compound predicate adjective.)

12. There are color schemes to choose and fabrics to select. (Underline the compound simple subject.)

13. Who likes the color yellow better, Teresa or Sandy? (Underline the subject.)

14. Just imagining a color scheme gives Ann pleasure. (Underline the indirect object.)

15. We consider that wallpaper pattern best. (Underline the objective complement.)

16. Selecting the right wallpaper for a room is a challenge. (Underline the predicate nominative.)

17. The Chinese invented the art of making paper. (Underline the verb.)

18. Actually, however, wallpapering a room was a French invention. (Underline the predicate nominative.)

19. This type of decoration first became fashionable in the late fifteenth century. (Underline the predicate adjective.)

20. Here are the pattern samples for the living room. (Underline the subject.)

Part 3: Identifying Phrases

On the line after each sentence, write whether the underlined portion of the sentence is a *prepositional phrase*, an *appositive phrase*, an *infinitive phrase*, a *gerund phrase*, a *participial phrase*, or a *nominative absolute*.

21. Sunning ourselves happily, we stretched out on towels. _____

22. It was marvelous to have discovered a pristine beach. _____

23. Soaking up the sun was a delightful sensation. _____

24. Far from the shore, two porpoises broke the water's surface. _____

25. Delighted by the playful animals, Mia watched through binoculars. _____

26. The porpoises having disappeared, we chatted and snoozed. _____

27. "Who's up for a swim?" asked Ben, a champion surfer. _____

28. What feels better than to plunge into the ocean on a hot day? _____

29. Around noon, we enjoyed a light picnic lunch. _____

30. We rested for an hour before going back in the water. _____

Part 4: Identifying Clauses and Types of Sentences

On the lines after each sentence, write whether the sentence is *simple, compound, complex,* or *compound-complex.* If the sentence contains any subordinate clauses, underline each subordinate clause and tell whether it is an *adjective* clause, an *adverb* clause, a *noun* clause, or an *elliptical* clause.

31. Amphibians, which include frogs, toads, and salamanders, are the most primitive terrestrial vertebrates.

   _____

32. Reptiles normally have scales, but the skin of amphibians is moist and usually scaleless.

   _____

33. This article informs me that the eggs of amphibians are softer than reptiles' eggs.

   _____

34. Many amphibians deposit their eggs in water; the water-breathing young develop into air breathers when they reach adulthood.

   _____

35. In contrast with amphibians, reptiles do not hatch in water but come out on land instead.

   _____

Part 5: Creating Effective Sentences

On the lines provided, rewrite the following sentences according to the directions in parentheses.

36. Sociologists have carried out studies, they indicate that pets are good for the elderly. (Correct the sentence error.)

   _____

   _____

37. Suffering from stress, benefits are often found if you get a pet. (Correct the misplaced modifier.)

_____

_____

38. Most people need companionship. Single elderly people often suffer from loneliness. (Combine with a comma and a coordinating conjunction.)

_____

_____

39. Some elderly people have only a few friends left in the neighborhood, others have trouble making new friends. (Correct the sentence error.)

_____

_____

40. Health experts have recommended that older people keep a pet for all these reasons. (Begin the sentence with a prepositional phrase.)

_____

_____

41. To care for a dog or a cat properly, special provisions must sometimes be made. (Correct the dangling modifier.)

_____

_____

42. An affectionate pet offers love. It also offers companionship. (Combine using a compound direct object.)

_____

_____

43. Cats are especially popular with older people. (Rewrite using inverted word order.)

_____

_____

44. On older people, the positive effect of pets is increasingly recognized by experts. (Correct the misplaced modifier.)

_____

_____

45. Have you seen a photograph of Mrs. Delaney's cats and the dogs belonging to Mr. Delgado? (Correct the faulty parallelism.)

_____

_____

Part 6: Supplying the Correct Verb

Circle the verb in parentheses that correctly completes each sentence.

46. If he (was, were) a lion, he would be a truly social wild cat.

47. Far more than leopards, cheetahs, or tigers, lions (seem, will seem) to enjoy living in groups called prides.

48. Living together in prides, lions are more successful hunters than they (would be, had been) if they hunted alone.

49. The strongest links in lion society (form, are forming) between mothers and daughters.

50. Thus, the females have always (lay, lain) at the core of any pride.

51. After they have (growed, grown) to the age of three or four, young males are forced to leave the pride.

52. This behavioral feature (appears, had appeared) to be nature's way of insuring genetic diversity.

53. A young male may have (led, lead) a nomadic life for several years before attaching himself to another, unrelated pride.

54. You can usually tell when the young male (was, is) challenging an older, more experienced male for leadership of the pride.

55. If the resident male is in poorer condition, the younger visitor usually (defeats, will defeat) him.

Part 7: Supplying the Correct Pronoun
Circle the pronoun in parentheses that correctly completes each sentence.

56. (We, Us) students like the music of the Beatles.

57. Jack and (she, her) both have their favorite Beatles songs.

58. The Beatles' harmonies seem ingenious to Jack and (she, her).

59. (Who, Whom), may I ask, has not heard of the song-writing team of John Lennon and Paul McCartney?

60. These were the two Beatles (who, whom) critics praised most.

61. Dad will play Beatles tapes for (whoever, whomever) will listen.

62. The biggest Beatles fans in town are Mom and (he, him).

63. Trish has little in common with (we, us) diehard fans.

64. Trish likes classical music more than (I, me).

65. The audience at her piano recital included many relatives of (her, hers).

Part 8: Making Words Agree
Circle the term in parentheses that correctly completes each sentence.

66. Many of my friends (is, are) interested in journalism and the media.

67. There (is, are) no one or nothing that can stop Wally from watching the evening news on television.

68. Ethics in journalism (is, are) an issue that interests Kim.

69. Paula thinks that the attention span of TV audiences (is, are) shorter than that of newspaper readers.

70. Given the round-the-clock nature of television news, often a large team of TV journalists (works, work) on a single story.

71. Joe is only one of several classmates who (has, have) contributed stories to our local paper.

72. People praise this magazine or that newspaper for (its, their) thoughtful articles.

73. Seventy-five cents (is, are) not a high price for a newspaper.

74. Every chart and diagram in that story (was, were) informative.

75. Either individual photos or a collage (illustrate, illustrates) a story effectively.

76. Everyone chose (his or her, their) favorite sections of the paper.

77. Lou and (I, myself) often get our news from the Internet.

78. There (is, are) now Web sites for many reliable news outlets.

79. Some Web sites are updated so frequently that (you, one) can find breaking news every few minutes.

80. Still more popular than any other medium as a source of news (is, are) television.

Part 9: Using Modifiers Correctly
Circle the term in parentheses that correctly completes each sentence.

81. Of all the antique shops in town, the one I visited last week is the (better, best).

82. The eighteenth-century desk cost more than (any, any other) item.

83. Brenda thought that the Indonesian shadow puppets were the (cutest, most cutest) items of all.

84. (Farther, Further) back, the store displayed fine costume jewelry.

85. Yolanda's interest in vintage clothing is greater than (Donna, Donna's).

86. Marilyn was (closer, more close) to buying than she realized.

87. The panels of stained glass on sale were stunning; I had never seen (complexer, more complex) designs.

88. The eighteenth-century china was (most unique, unique).

89. Of all the garden gnomes I've seen, those were the (most bad, worst).

90. Ben knows more about antiques than (anyone, anyone else) I know.

Part 10: Eliminating Usage Errors
Circle the term in parentheses that correctly completes each sentence.

91. Haven't you (ever, never) seen a tern?

92. Do terns live (anywhere, anywheres) near your home?

93. You scarcely (ever, never) see terns far from coastal regions.

94. (Except, Accept) for a handful, most terns live by water.

95. A single tern egg (lay, laid) in the nest.

96. Of all birds, Arctic terns migrate the (farthest, furthest).

97. Terns communicate with (each other, one another) by using distinctive calls.

98. (Everyone, Every one) of those tern colonies is located in a marsh or along a river.

99. By October, the Arctic tern is (already, all ready) on the move from the northern hemisphere to Antarctica.

100. Share this information about terns (among, between) your friends.

Part 11: Proofreading for Capitalization
Circle the letters that should be capitalized.

101. the italian city of pisa has a world-famous monument.

102. haven't you seen cousin norm's photographs of the leaning tower of pisa?

103. norm and his brothers, skip and paul, took the pictures when they visited italy in august 1997.

104. in history class we learned about another famous european landmark, the eiffel tower in paris, france.

105. this structure was designed by the french engineer alexandre gustave eiffel for the paris exposition of 1889.

106. my aunt alice asked mom if the exposition was held in spring, summer, or fall.

107. about ten years before the eiffel tower opened, workers in new york city were busy building the brooklyn bridge.

108. here is what i know about it: this bridge spans the east river to join the boroughs of brooklyn and manhattan.

109. does the bridge start on the brooklyn side at the corner of flatbush and fulton avenues?

110. rona asked dr. petry, "is sharpe's baby food manufactured near prospect park in brooklyn?"

Part 12: Using Correct Punctuation

On the lines provided, rewrite the sentences, correcting all errors in punctuation.

111. Winslow Homer 1836–1910 who is often said to rank among America's finest painters was born in Boston Massachusetts.

_____

_____

112. Homer showed artistic talent as a child but nineteenth century Boston offered its residents few opportunities for training in art.

_____

_____

113. In a dissatisfying period of apprenticeship Homer worked for a two year stint with a Boston lithographer.

_____

_____

114. Didnt he then decide to move to New York City where he hoped to make a career as an illustrator.

_____

_____

115. Homer attended night classes in drawing illustrating and oil painting.

_____

_____

116. Then he won an assignment from the magazine Harper's Weekly to cover the Civil War as an artist illustrator.

_____

_____

117. Homers war sketches which he later converted into engravings and oil paintings often focused on the soldiers daily routine in camp.

_____

_____

118. The artists notable Civil War paintings include the following The Brierwood Pipe 1864 The Bright Side 1865 and A Rainy Day in Camp 1871.

_____

_____

119. Here is a reproduction of another of Homers masterpieces The Veteran in a New Field.

_____

_____

120. In France after the war Homer was influenced by the Barbizon School a group of preImpressionist French painters who did landscapes in a realistic style.

_____

_____

121. As this pamphlet Homers Art explains Homer abandoned illustration in 1876 and devoted the rest of his career to oil painting and watercolors.

_____

_____

122. Among his best known works you have probably seen some of them before are his paintings of the sea.

_____

_____

123. Some of Homers watercolors, said our art teacher Mr. Gonzaga, are as good as his best oil paintings.

_____

_____

124. Mark asked What is your favorite seascape by Homer Alice.

_____

125. If I had to make a choice, Alice replied, it would be The Fog Warning.

_____

_____

Part III:
Academic and
Workplace Skills

Assessment for Chapter 28: Speaking, Listening, Viewing, and Representing

1. Circle the letter of the answer that represents the best type of preparation for communicating effectively in a group discussion. On the line, explain your answer.
   a. Ask questions politely, if you need clarification or explanation.
   b. Bring up a subject even if it has only a remote relationship to the topic at hand.
   c. Take a position and stick to it.
   d. Speak honestly and forcefully, even if you risk offending someone in the group.
   _____

2. Imagine that your class is having a discussion about the need to increase participation in after-school activities. Write a question that would be *relevant* to the discussion. Then, explain why the question is relevant.
   _____
   _____

3. Circle the letter of the answer that best represents an *effective* statement for a student to make about the condition of the school hallways. On the line, explain why your answer is preferable to the others.
   a. Let's agree to remind each other to pick up litter when we see it.
   b. Other people in our school are really sloppy.
   c. I blame not only students, but also teachers, for the condition of the hallways.
   d. No one seems to care very much about how the school looks.
   _____

4. Match the definition with the type of speech it describes.

   _____ informative   a. a speech that tries to convince an audience

   _____ extemporaneous   b. a speech that provides amusement or enjoyment

   _____ persuasive   c. a speech that provides facts

   _____ entertaining   d. a speech delivered with no prepared manuscript

5. Which of the above speeches would you give if you were presenting the results of a test on the ground water in your local streams? Explain your answer.
   _____
   _____

6. Which kind of speech would you give if you had just been given an award that you didn't expect? Explain your answer.
   _____
   _____

Use the following information to answer questions 7 and 8.

> You have decided to try to encourage a better relationship between your high school and the store owners in the surrounding streets. Store owners complain about teenagers being too noisy in the stores and driving away other customers. High school students complain that the store owners don't seem to value them as customers.

7. Where would you go to gather additional information about the problem? Explain your answer.
   _____
   _____

8. You have spoken to some of the store owners, and they are willing to cooperate, if students will also cooperate. You are preparing a speech. Fill in the note card below with your main points.

```
┌─────────────────────────────────────────────────────────────┐
│                                                               │
│  Problem:                                                     │
│                                                               │
│  Students' Viewpoint:                                         │
│                                                               │
│  Store Owners' Viewpoint:                                     │
│                                                               │
│  Reason for Trying to Solve Problem:                          │
│                                                               │
│  Possible Solution:                                           │
│                                                               │
└─────────────────────────────────────────────────────────────┘
```

9. Circle the letter of the answer that represents a *nonverbal strategy* that might be used when delivering a speech. On the line, explain your answer.
   a. Make sure that everyone can see you well.
   b. Speak loudly, confidently, and clearly.
   c. Use hand gestures for emphasis.
   d. Practice your speech before you deliver it.
   _____

10. Imagine that you are evaluating someone else's speech.
    a. If you are analyzing *what* was said, write a comment or question that you might have.

    _____

    b. If you are analyzing *how* it was said, write a comment or question that you might have.

    _____

11. Explain why making eye contact with the audience is considered important when a speaker is addressing a group.

    _____

    _____

12. Name one way that you can evaluate your understanding of a speech that you have just heard.

    _____

13. Match the definition with the kind of listening it describes.

    _____ critical   a. analyze aesthetic or artistic elements

    _____ empathic   b. imagine yourself in the speaker's position

    _____ appreciative   c. listen for facts and supporting details

    _____ reflective   d. ask questions and think about the responses

14. Write the letter of the kind of listening next to the type of communication it describes.

    _____ class discussion   a. empathic

    _____ family conversation b. appreciative

    _____ poetry reading   c. reflective

    _____ announcement   d. critical

15. Imagine that someone has just given a speech about the increase in the number of drivers who are speeding through the center of town.
    a. Give an example of a question that you might ask that calls for clarification.

    _____

    b. Give an example of a question that you might ask that calls for support.

    _____

    c. Give an example of an open-ended question that you might ask.

    _____

    d. Give an example of a closed question that you might ask.

    _____

16. Which of the following is the best way to test yourself on how well you listened to information presented in a speech? Circle the letter that corresponds with your choice. Then, explain your answer.
    a. You can paraphrase key points and share them with someone to check their accuracy.
    b. You can paraphrase key points and read them to yourself.
    c. You can see whether you have committed most of the speech to memory.
    d. You can ask your friends what they remember.

    _____

17. Circle the letter of the answer that describes information conveyed by a historical map. On the line, explain your answer.
    a. the weather patterns of a country
    b. the battles that have taken place during a particular war
    c. the climate of a country
    d. the population of a particular city

    _____

Answer questions 18 and 19 by referring to the map below.

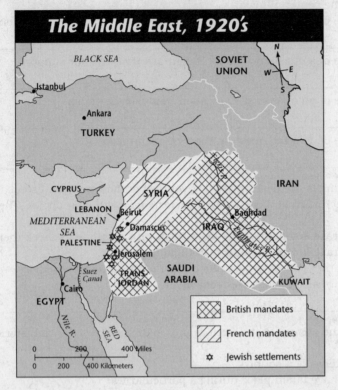

18. From looking at this map, what can you infer about the European presence in the Middle East in the 1920's?

_____

19. Speculate about a possible agricultural advantage in the location of the Jewish settlements. Explain your answer.

_____

_____

20. A line graph illustrates changes over time. Circle the letter of an example of information that could be expressed well in a line graph. On the line, explain your answer.
   a. the difference between oil consumption in two countries in a single day
   b. a comparison between the money two different countries spent on education in a year
   c. a current sales analysis of three computer companies
   d. the change in the number of immigrants to the United States in a twenty-year period

_____

21. A bar graph compares and contrasts amounts. Circle the letter of an example of information that could be expressed well in a bar graph. On the line, explain your answer.
   a. how politically unstable nations have increased their debt
   b. obstacles to progress in developing nations
   c. causes of environmental challenges
   d. the number of qualified physicians in ten different countries

_____

22. Imagine that you are the manager of a textile export company. What might be a reason to use a pie graph to analyze the quantity of fabric your company sent to France, Japan, and Australia during the current year?

_____

23. Match the content with the medium in which you would expect to find it.

    _____ interview   a. brief summaries with video footage

    _____ commercial   b. questions and answers

    _____ Web page   c. short message of images and slogans

    _____ television news   d. up-to-date interactive content

24. Match the example with the type of persuasion it illustrates.

    _____ loaded language   a. a photograph of a baby with a tear running down her cheek

    _____ bias   b. "A mouth-watering slice of Mrs. Jones's delectable cake will take your cares away."

    _____ slogan   c. European cars are simply better than American cars.

    _____ loaded images   d. "We try harder!"

25. Circle the letter of the answer that is *not* an example of how you might interpret fine art such as a painting, drawing, or piece of sculpture. On the line, explain your answer.
    a. determining which shapes or images you can discern
    b. determining how the artist uses light and shadows
    c. determining where the artist buys his or her materials
    d. determining the overall feeling conveyed by the work

    _____

26. Which form would you use to present the information below—a chart, a map, or an illustration? Explain your answer.

    London in Flames

    The Nazi blitz of London raged for two months in 1940. Each night, German bombers dropped tons of bombs, igniting fires that burned out of control. Each morning, Londoners picked through the rubble and counted the dead. The blitz destroyed some of the city's most precious buildings, but it failed to break the will of the English people.

    _____

    _____

    _____

27. Imagine you are creating a poster to ask for help with finding a lost animal.
    a. Where on the poster would you list the most important information?

    _____

    b. How would you make the poster visually noticeable, so that people would pay attention to it?

    _____

28. Imagine that you are going to give an oral presentation on the architecture of Shakespeare's Globe Theatre and that you want to enhance your presentation by using multimedia. Select two of the options below and explain how you would use them.

                slides   videotape   music   art   models

    _____

    _____

    _____

29. Circle the letter of an element that a shooting script for a video would need to have in order for the crew to know what the scenery should look like. On the line, explain your answer.
    a. instructions for transitions
    b. dialogue
    c. descriptions of camera angles
    d. descriptions of sets

    _____

30. Imagine that you are going to perform an interpretive dance, based on a tragic love story. First, identify the mood you would try to establish. Then, describe the lighting and music you would use.

    _____

    _____

    _____

    _____

Assessment for Chapter 29: Vocabulary and Spelling

1. Circle the letter of the answer that describes a good way to expand your vocabulary. On the line, explain your answer.
    a. drawing a graph
    b. creating a diagram
    c. writing a shopping list
    d. reading a magazine article

    _____

2. The following paragraph contains five underlined words. As you read the passage, circle the context clues that help you to determine the meaning of each word. Then, in the items below, underline the correct meaning of the word, based upon how it was used in the passage.

    One of the <u>inescapable</u> facts of life that students have to adjust to is taking tests. Especially in the <u>contemporary</u> world around us, where achievement in school can be a <u>determinant</u> that affects the college a student can get into, it is important to <u>endeavor</u> with your best efforts. If you have high <u>aspirations</u>, you have to work hard to reach them.

    a. unlikely; inevitable
    b. present-day; equal
    c. reason; factor
    d. try; cease
    e. breaths; goals

3. Underline the example of figurative language in the sentence below. On the line, explain its meaning.

    Delilah was ecstatic about her birthday, and her face was full of sunshine.

    _____

4. Underline the example of an idiom in the sentence below. On the line, explain its meaning.

    Jon wanted to express his opinion in the meeting, but he was afraid to rock the boat.

    _____

5. Circle the letter of the sentence below that uses the word *relic* as a technical term. On the line, explain your answer.
    a. Michael complained that he was tired of driving his parents' *relic* to school.
    b. David had had the car for years, but he couldn't bring himself to get rid of the *relic*.
    c. Rich found an ancient *relic* on his last archeological dig in the caves of Akabah.
    d. Katie felt that the city train she was riding in needed to be replaced, because it was a *relic*.

    _____

6. a. Give the denotation (the literal meaning) of the word *vital* as it is used in the following sentence.

    As a routine part of the examination, Dr. Samson checked her patient's *vital* signs.

    _____

    b. Give the connotation (the meaning that includes judgments and feelings) of the word *vital* as it is used in the following passage.

    Parents don't always understand that sometimes talking to a friend on the phone can be *vital* for your emotional well-being.

    _____

7. The word *benevolent* means "disposed to dispense good works and goodwill." Circle the letter of the word that is the best synonym for *benevolent*. On the line, use *benevolent* in a sentence.
   a. charitable
   b. miserly
   c. abundant
   d. narrow-minded

   _____

8. The word *zenith* means "the highest point." Circle the letter of the word that is an antonym for *zenith*. On the line, use *zenith* in a sentence.
   a. peak
   b. summit
   c. vertical
   d. depths

   _____

9. Fill in the following chart. First, complete the second word pair, so that it has the same relationship as the first word pair. Then, describe the relationship. The first line has been done as an example.

Word Pair #1	Word Pair #2	Relationship
airplane : wing	fireplace : brick	whole to part
cub : bear	_____ : cat	
sculptor : statue	composer : _____	
fish : water	bird : _____	
softness : loudness	hysterical : _____	

10. Circle the letter of the answer that best completes the analogy below. On the line, explain the word-pair relationship.
    DISCOVER : FIND :: BEGIN :
    a. unearth
    b. undo
    c. end
    d. start

    _____

11. Choose one of the following techniques—keeping a vocabulary notebook, making flashcards, or reading vocabulary words into a tape recorder—and describe how it can help you expand your vocabulary.

    _____

12. a. Select one of the following kinds of information contained in a dictionary, and explain how it is useful to a student who is reading a textbook.
       the syllables of a word   a word's part of speech   word origin   synonyms for a word

       _____

    b. Select one of the kinds of information above, and explain how it might be useful to a student who is writing an essay.

       _____

13. One of the origins of the word *haul* is from the Middle English word *halen*, meaning "to pull." It also derives from the Old English word *geholian*, meaning "to obtain." Use this information to write a sentence using the word *haul*.

_____

14. Circle the letter corresponding to the best choice. A thesaurus
    a. provides synonyms and words that have a similar meaning to the word you are looking up
    b. lists different definitions or meanings of words
    c. lists word origins
    d. notes parts of speech and pronunciations

15. Read the italicized word below, paying attention to its meaning in the context of the sentence. Then, circle the letter of the best synonym for the word, as used in the sentence.

    Fran was steady and fun to be around most of the time; however, sometimes she could be *volatile* and become easily annoyed.

    a. reliable
    b. sluggish
    c. unstable
    d. indifferent

16. Most textbooks contain a glossary at the end of the book to help define words that are specific to the content of the book. Circle the letter of the word that you might expect to find in the glossary of a geography text. On the line, explain your answer.
    a. peninsula
    b. statement
    c. ratio
    d. cause

_____

17. The root *-port-* means "to carry." How does knowing the meaning of this root help you to understand the meaning of the words *portable* and *transport*?

_____

_____

18. Read each group of words below. Write the *root* that the words share, and write the suggested meaning of each root.

Word	Root	Meaning of the Root
sensible, sentiment	_____	_____
monologue, monotone	_____	_____
chronicle, chronological	_____	_____

19. Read each group of words below, and write the *prefix* that the words share. Next to the prefix, write its meaning.

Word	Prefix	Meaning of the Prefix
subconscious, submerge	_____	_____
misinterpret, mistake	_____	_____
unfinished, unforgivable	_____	_____

20. Read each group of words below, and write the *suffix* that the words share. Next to the suffix, write its meaning.

Word	Suffix	Meaning of the Suffix
beautiful, wonderful	_____	_____
penniless, loveless	_____	_____
adaptable, portable	_____	_____

21. Words can be combined to create new words. Match one word from the first column with the correct word from the second column to form a combined word. Write each new word and its meaning on the lines provided.

green   gate
sand   come
tail   paper
over   house

_____

_____

_____

_____

22. Identify the spelling rule for *ie* and *ei* words.

_____

_____

23. Match the definition with the step for remembering a spelling word it describes.

_____ Look   a. Notice arrangements or visual word patterns.

_____ Pronounce   b. Repeat the word until you can write it correctly.

_____ Write   c. Say the word aloud.

_____ Review   d. Put the word on paper and check it in the dictionary.

24. Read the following spelling rules.
   a. Most words that end in *y* preceded by a consonant change *y* to *i* before a suffix is added.
   b. Most words that end in *y* preceded by a vowel do not change when a suffix is added. Now, add suffixes and create new words from the roots below.

portray + -ing _____

merry + -ment _____

enjoy + -ment _____

apply + -ance _____

25. Adding a prefix does not change the spelling of a word. Form new words below by adding prefixes.

dis- + appear _____

mis- + inform _____

un- + expected _____

in- + appropriate _____

26. The plural forms of the words below follow the rule *either* for a) words that end in *y* or *o* preceded by a vowel (for which you add -*s*); or b) words that end in *y* preceded by a consonant (for which you change the *y* to *i* and add -*es*). Write the plural forms of the words.

    mystery _____

    party _____

    alley _____

    tragedy _____

    turkey _____

27. Read the following rules.
    a. Compound words follow the general rules for forming plurals. (Examples: *notebooks, firemen*.)
    b. For compound words with hyphens or compound words written as separate words, make the *modified* word plural. (Examples: *passers-by, suits of armor*.)
    Now, write the plural form for each of the following words.

    mother-in-law _____

    Canadian goose _____

    all-star _____

    country mouse _____

28. Read the sentences below to find the correct homophone. Underline the word that is correct in the context of the sentence.
    a. It was a tough *(knight, night)* to be outside.
    b. We couldn't tell from one minute to the next when it was going to *(rain, reign)* again.
    c. It was the worst *(whether, weather)* we had experienced in years.
    d. I don't know *(weather, whether)* I can stand another evening like that.

29. How can studying a foreign language help students with the spelling and pronunciation of English words?

    _____

    _____

30. Proofread the following passage. Circle the correctly spelled words in parentheses, and write them on the lines below.

    Sometimes, people forget that living in a (democrasy, democracy) is an opportunity to (exercise,

    excercise) their rights. Voting is just one of the many (privileges, priviledges) of living in a free society.

    Another is free speech. People sometimes take the (couragaeous, courageous) step of speaking out

    on unpopular issues, even though their (opinion, opinyon) may not be well (received, recieved).

    _____

    _____

    _____

    _____

    _____

30 Assessment for Chapter 30: Reading Skills

1. Match the definition with the textbook section it describes.

   _____ Table of contents   a. lists subjects with page numbers in back of book

   _____ Preface   b. charts, documents, or other material in back of book

   _____ Appendix   c. introduction

   _____ Index   d. lists books and other sources in back of book

   _____ Glossary   e. shows how the book is organized

   _____ Bibliography   f. lists terms and definitions in back of book

2. Describe why it is useful to a reader to have large titles and boldfaced headings at the beginning of each section of a textbook and throughout each chapter.

   _____

   _____

3. Explain why previewing the exercises and questions in a textbook chapter *before* you read the chapter can help you prepare for reading.

   _____

   _____

4. How does a caption under a picture help the reader?

   _____

Answer questions 5–7 by referring to the following excerpt for information.

France Falls. . .
The Battle of Britain

   With the fall of France, Britain stood alone [against Germany]. Hitler was sure that the British would sue [ask] for peace. But Winston Churchill, who had replaced Neville Chamberlain as prime minister, had other plans. For many years, Churchill had been a lone voice against the Nazi threat. In 1940, he rallied the British to fight on: "We shall defend our island, whatever the cost may be. We shall fight on the beaches, we shall fight on the landing grounds, we shall fight in the fields and in the streets, we shall fight in the hills; we shall never surrender."

5. *Skim* the excerpt—read the boldface headings and topic sentence—and write down the basic information covered by the passage.

   _____

   _____

6. *Scan* the excerpt—look through the text for key words—and write down information that you might use if you were taking quick notes for a research paper.

   _____

   _____

7. *Closely read* the excerpt—carefully read to find details that support the main idea or ideas—and write down information that would provide a deeper understanding of the subject matter.

   _____

   _____

   _____

8. How would you decide which of the three reading strategies—skimming, scanning, or close reading—to use before you begin to read a textbook passage?

_____

9. Match the definition with the question-answer relationship (QAR) it describes.

_____ Right There   a. Answers are not in the text; you rely on your experiences.

_____ Think and Search   b. You relate what the author says to what you know.

_____ Author and You   c. The answer is in the text, but you have to ponder the question and find evidence to support your answer.

_____ On Your Own   d. The answers are in the text in one or two sentences.

Read the following excerpt. Then, answer questions 10–12.

The English Bill of Rights

When the Catholic King, James II, was forced from the English throne in 1688, Parliament offered the Crown to his Protestant daughter Mary and her husband William of Orange. But Parliament insisted that William and Mary submit to a Bill of Rights. This document, a continuation of the struggle between the Crown and Parliament, sums up the powers that Parliament had been seeking since the Petition of Right in 1628.

10. Write down a *question* that might arise after you have read the boldface heading.

_____

_____

11. Write down a possible *answer* to your question, based on the information in the excerpt.

_____

_____

12. *Record* notes by writing down two important details from the excerpt.

_____

_____

13. Use the following information to help you fill in the sample outline below.

Development of Parliament

During the 1200's, English rulers often called on the Great Council for advice. Eventually, this body evolved into Parliament. Its name comes from the French word *parler*, which means "to talk." As Parliament acquired a larger role in government, it helped unify England.

In 1295, Edward I summoned Parliament to approve money for his wars in France. "What touches all," he declared, "should be approved by all." He had representatives of the "common people" join the lords and clergy. The "commons" [commoners] included two knights from each county and representatives of the towns.

. . . In time, Parliament developed into a two-house body; the House of Lords with nobles and high clergy and the House of Commons with knights and middle-class citizens.

I. Main Idea: _____

   A. Major Detail: _____

      1. Supporting Detail: _____

      2. Supporting Detail: _____

   B. Major Detail: _____

      1. Supporting Detail: _____

      2. Supporting Detail: _____

14. Imagine that you have to trace the history of the monarchy in Great Britain. Explain how you would use a chart, timeline, or diagram to show your information.

_____

_____

15. Think of two people with whom you are in a class, club, or other activity. Consider the following: two qualities (such as hair color, musical talent, or an interest in sports) they might have in common; and two ways in which each person is unique. Fill in the diagram below to illustrate the points of similarity and differences between these two individuals.

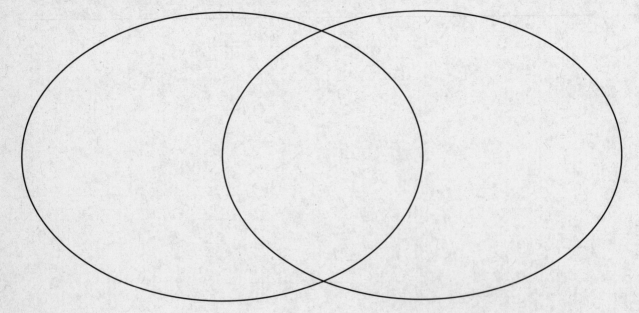

Name _____

Read the passage below to help you answer the questions 16–18.

> Like King Edward I, later English monarchs summoned Parliament for their own purposes. Over the centuries, though, Parliament gained the crucial "power of the purse." That is, it won the right to approve any new taxes. With that power, Parliament could insist that the monarch meet its demands before voting for taxes. In this way, it could check, or limit, the power of the monarch.

16. Make an inference about how the balance of power in Great Britain changed over time.

_____

_____

17. Write a fact about how Parliament's power changed.

_____

18. Write an opinion—from the viewpoint of either a monarch or a member of Parliament—about the changes in the powers given to Parliament.

_____

_____

19. Read the sentences below. In the space provided, indicate whether each sentence offers fact or opinion.

_____ People in Germany allowed a great mistake to occur when they enabled Hitler to come to power.

_____ World War II ended in 1945.

_____ After World War II, Germany was divided into sections controlled by the French, British, Americans, and Russians.

_____ The American bombing of Hiroshima could have been avoided.

20. Read the following passage. Write a follow-up sentence that uses *inductive reasoning* (drawing a conclusion or a generalization from the facts).

> Serena tested the pond water in three different locations. In all three locations, the pond water was found to contain a high level of nitrogen. She also noticed pieces of algae floating on the surface of the pond.

_____

21. Use the following information to create statements based on *deductive reasoning*, using the three-part formula of a *syllogism*.

> I enjoy eating citrus fruits, because they are filled with Vitamin C. Vitamin C is good for your general health, as it helps your system to fight infection. Two of the citrus fruits I enjoy eating most are oranges and grapefruits. I also enjoy lemons and limes. I also like to eat melons, which have Vitamin C, even though they are not citrus fruits.

Major premise (Generalization): _____

Minor premise (Apply generalization to a specific case): _____

Conclusion: _____

22. Read the following examples. Write whether each one is an example of *good logic* or represents a *logical fallacy*.

    a. Susannah always catches the softball successfully with one hand, so she's obviously a good softball player. _____

    b. Last week, Ralph missed a catch, so he's a bad athlete. _____

    c. Barbara got distracted and burned dinner last week. She's a poor cook. _____

    d. Jonathan made delicious chicken soup; he knows how to combine herbs and spices. _____

23. Read the following examples. Write whether each one is an example of *cause-and-effect reasoning* or *unrelated events*.

    a. Since I washed my car yesterday, it rained all day today. _____

    b. Sarah worked hard all year; in June, she ended the year with excellent grades. _____

    c. I'm glad I wished all year for good things to happen to me, because I won a raffle last week. _____

    d. Amy has been practicing very hard, so she can now play a complicated drum solo. _____

24. The following sentence has a *denotative* (literal and neutral) meaning. Rewrite it using words that convey a *connotative* (implied positive or negative) meaning.
    I planted three different-colored tulip bulbs last fall, and this spring they have started to grow.

    _____

    _____

25. The following passage has a particular *connotative* tone. Rewrite it using *denotative* words to give it a more neutral tone.

    The new ice cream shop has an unbelievable variety of flavors—chocolate truffle, raspberry fluff, and almond delight. Of course, they also sell coffee, vanilla, and strawberry. And each bite of creamy, smooth ice cream goes down your throat ever so gently.

    _____

    _____

    _____

26. Rewrite the sentence below to eliminate the inflated language.

    After much corporate strategizing, the manager of the department has decided to implement a re-structuring of the overall design of the working environment, guaranteeing an additional several inches of space in all of the divided rectangular or squared-off areas inhabited by members of the work force team.

    _____

    _____

27. Rewrite the sentence below to eliminate the euphemism.

    After several hours of lingering in calm repose, Laura's canary finally passed on to a more peaceful place.

    _____

    _____

28. Rewrite the sentence below so that it is less slanted.

     A tremendous amount of backbreaking effort has gone into the production of this timely and informative report.

     _____

     _____

29. Read the following sentence and answer the questions below.

     "I question whether God himself would wish me to hide behind the principle of nonviolence while innocent persons were being slaughtered."

     —Bishop Abel Muzorewa

     a. What seems to be the author's purpose in this quotation?

     _____

     b. Do you feel he accomplishes his purpose? Explain your answer.

     _____

30. a. What does it mean to *identify* with a character or a situation in a work of fiction?

     _____

     b. Give an example of a work of fiction you have identified with, and briefly explain why you identified with it.

     _____

     _____

     _____

31. Explain how *symbols* (elements of a story that represent a larger idea) or *allusions* (indirect or implied references to something or someone outside a story) can add to a reader's appreciation of a work of fiction.

     _____

     _____

32. a. Describe an element of drama that is distinct from other works of the imagination.

     _____

     b. How can a reader make a drama come alive in his or her mind?

     _____

33. Describe one way reading a poem aloud can enhance your appreciation for this form of literature.

     _____

     What is one benefit of identifying the imagery in a poem?

     _____

34. Give an example of how reading old diaries, letters, or speeches might increase a student's understanding of an important moment in history.

     _____

35. Circle the letter of the answer that describes a situation in which newspapers would be a good resource. On the line, explain your answer.
     a. Students have to debate the wisdom of America's intervention in another country.
     b. Students have to decide which academic courses to take for the upcoming year.
     c. Students have to translate and analyze a French poem.
     d. Students have to analyze the impact of the invention of the steam engine.

     _____

Assessment for Chapter 31: Study, Reference, and Test-Taking Skills

1. Give an example of a good study skill, and explain how the skill helps students improve school performance.

   _____

   _____

2. Fill in the study plan diagram below with one idea for creating an effective study area, one idea for keeping a study schedule that helps you to stay organized, and one idea for setting up a study notebook.

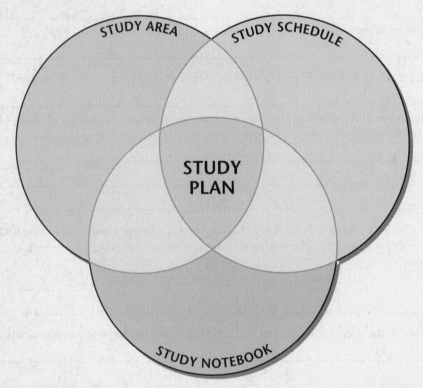

3. Name one way in which you could improve the study plan you have been using this year.

   _____

Refer to the following passage to answer questions 4–6 below.

   Between 1337 and 1453, England and France fought a series of conflicts, known as the Hundred Years' War. The fighting devastated France and drained England.
   English rulers had battled for centuries to hold onto the French lands of their Norman ancestors. French kings, for their part, were intent on extending their own power in France. When Edward III of England claimed the French Crown in 1337, war erupted anew between these rival powers. Once fighting started, economic rivalry and a growing sense of national pride made it hard for either side to give up the struggle.

4. Create a modified outline of this passage by writing the main idea and listing three details under it.

_____

_____

_____

_____

5. Write a brief summary of the above passage.

_____

_____

_____

_____

6. Write the topic sentence of your summary.

_____

_____

7. a. Give an example of the kind of information found in card, printed, or electronic catalogs that can help you to locate library books.

_____

   b. Give one reason explaining why card catalogs have three kinds of cards (author, title, and subject).

_____

8. Circle the letter of the answer that indicates how an *electronic* library catalog can best assist a student doing research on the current status of the monarchy's power in Great Britain. On the line, explain your answer.
   a. The student can see if a book is on the library shelves or has been checked out.
   b. The student can locate all related books available in libraries in other cities.
   c. The student can find out how many books on Ireland are in his or her local library.
   d. The student can ask a reference librarian where the encyclopedias are located.

_____

9. a. What types of books are classified using the Dewey Decimal System—fiction or

   nonfiction? _____
   b. Name one reason why the Dewey Decimal System divides information into ten major areas.

_____

10. In your school or public library, would you expect to find the novel *Tale of Two Cities*, by Charles Dickens, on a shelf that starts with *Di-* or *Ta-*? Explain your answer.

_____

_____

11. In your school or public library, would you expect to find a biography of Charles Dickens, by Catherine Peters, on a shelf that starts with *Di-* or *Pe-*? Explain your answer.

_____

_____

Use the information below to answer questions 12–14.

> You have been assigned to write a research paper about *Sputnik,* the unmanned satellite sent into orbit by the U.S.S.R. in 1957.

12. Circle the letter of the subject under which you might find the most useful information for your topic. On the line, explain your answer.
    a. the political struggles of the Russian people
    b. developments in space exploration during the twentieth century
    c. astronomy
    d. American spaceship construction in the 1950's
    _____

13. Which class of the Dewey Decimal System would you be most likely to refer to while conducting your research on *Sputnik?*
    a. literature
    b. general works
    c. philosophy
    d. technology

14. List two types of reference sources you might investigate to research *Sputnik.*
    _____

15. If you were writing a research paper on the latest developments in animal cloning, would you use primarily reference books or periodicals (newspapers, magazines, and journals)? Explain your answer.
    _____
    _____
    _____

16. a. The *vertical file* in a library holds information that is not suitable for being shelved, such as pamphlets, booklets, photographs, or original magazine or newspaper clippings. How could this information be of use when researching a historical subject?
    _____

    b. A *citation* in a periodical index tells you where and when an article was published. Why is this information important?
    _____

17. A sample entry from the *Readers' Guide to Periodical Literature* on the subject of skydiving might include a cross-reference to professional stuntmen. Explain how you might use this cross-reference, if your research topic was skydiving.
    _____
    _____

18. Identify the type of dictionary—abridged, unabridged, or specialized—you would use in each of the following situations.

    a. to look up the medical term *labyrinthitis* _____

    b. to check the pronunciation of a word, in preparation for speaking on a national television show __

    c. to find the word origins as well as all of the different meanings of the word *board* _____

19. Place the following four words under the appropriate pair of guide words indicating where they would be found in a dictionary:

vocal　　　voluminous　　　vision　　　volume

void—vortex	volume—voted	vocabulary—voice	virtue—vital

20. A dictionary entry tells you how to pronounce a word. Tell how information about pronunciation is useful to a reader, a writer, or a speaker.

_____

_____

Use the dictionary entry to answer the following three questions.

> **vol·ley** (väl´ē) n. pl. -leys [[MF *volee* flight, fr. *voler* to fly, fr. L *volare*]] a) a flight of missiles (as arrows) b) simultaneous discharge of a number of missile weapons c) one round per gun in a battery fired as soon as a gun is ready without regard to order d) (1) the flight of the ball (as in volleyball or tennis) *also* a return of the ball before it touches the ground (2) the kick of the ball in soccer before it rebounds.

21. Which syllable is accented in *volley*? _____

22. Write two sentences, using a different definition of the word *volley* for each sentence.

_____

_____

23. Describe how the definitions of the Middle French word *volee* and the French word *voler* relate to one of the current definitions of *volley*.

_____

_____

24. Which of the following reference works—an atlas, an almanac, an encyclopedia, or a thesaurus—would you use to find the information for each item below? Write your answers on the lines.

a. names of the current political parties in Scotland _____

b. information on the climate in Bath, England _____

c. a synonym for *monarchy* _____

d. a background article on the Potato Famine in Ireland _____

25. How can using videotapes of documentaries or news programs enhance students' research experiences?

_____

_____

26. Give an example of one way you might evaluate the reliability of a Web site.

_____

27. Circle the letter that corresponds with the best method for previewing a test before taking it. On the line, explain why your choice is correct and the others are not.
a. Supply the best single answer.
b. Check to make sure that you have followed directions precisely.
c. Answer the easy questions first.
d. Skim the test to get an overview of the questions.

_____

28. Sometimes you are instructed to skip test questions when you are unsure of the answers. Give one reason explaining why you might be given this instruction.

_____

_____

Refer to this passage to answer the following four questions.

> In the century after the Glorious Revolution [1688], three new political institutions arose in Britain: political parties, the cabinet, and the office of prime minister. The appearance of these institutions was part of the evolution of England's constitutional government—that is, a government whose power is defined and limited by law. Unlike the United States Constitution, which is a single written document, the British Constitution is made up of all acts of Parliament over the centuries. It also includes documents such as the Magna Carta and Bill of Rights, as well as unwritten traditions that protect citizens rights.
>
> Two political parties emerged in England in the late 1600's, Tories and Whigs. The conservative Tories were generally landed [land-owning] aristocrats who sought to preserve older traditions. They supported broad royal powers and a dominant Anglican Church [the Church of England]. The Whigs backed the more liberal policies of the Glorious Revolution. They were more likely to reflect urban business interests, support religious toleration for Protestants, and favor Parliament over the Crown. For much of the 1700's, the Whigs dominated Parliament.

29. Write the letter of description next to the item from the passage it describes.

    _____ 1. Whigs   a. a document in the British Constitution

    _____ 2. Magna Carta   b. a political party that favored royal powers

    _____ 3. Anglican Church   c. a political party that favored religious tolerance

    _____ 4. Tories   d. the Church of England

30. Circle the letter of the best response. On the line, write the clue from the passage that helped you to determine the answer.
    The British Constitution:
    a. was not terribly useful in defining the role of the Parliament.
    b. is like the United States Constitution.
    c. has several documents and unwritten traditions.
    d. tended to favor the power of the Crown.

    _____

31. Indicate whether the following statements are true or false, based upon the information in the passage.

    _____ a. The English aristocrats were successful businessmen who worked in the city.

    _____ b. Religious tolerance was a concern in England in the 1700's.

    _____ c. The Whigs were more powerful in Parliament than the Tories in the 1700's.

    _____ d. The Whigs and Tories favored essentially the same practices.

32. Complete the following sentence.
    The appearance in England of political parties, a cabinet, and the establishment of the office of prime minister represented the development of a government that would thereafter be ruled

    by _____

33. Circle the letter of the answer that is an example of an analogy based on an *antonym* relationship. On the line, give another example of a pair of antonyms.
    a. salmon : fish
    b. keyboard : piano
    c. computer : monitor
    d. release : capture

    _____

34. Circle the letter of the pair of words that has the same analogy relationship as the first pair. On the line, describe the relationship between the words.
    COURAGE : SUPERHERO ::
    a. enthusiasm : sports fan
    b. shyness : neighbor
    c. fear : friend
    d. pity : compassion

    _____

35. Which of the following techniques would you suggest to someone *preparing* for a standardized test, such as the PSAT, SAT, or ACT? Circle the letter of the best answer. On the line, explain why your answer is correct and the others are not.
    a. Go back and look again at any answers you omitted.
    b. Fill in each bubble on the answer sheet completely.
    c. Skip questions you cannot answer.
    d. Practice on sample tests in the weeks or months leading up to the test.

    _____

(32) Assessment for Chapter 32: Workplace Skills and Competencies

1. Give an example of how a student could practice becoming more effective in one-on-one communication.

_____

Read the following scenario. Then, answer questions 2–4.

> There is a summer job that appeals to you, because it is at a day camp. You enjoy working with younger children, and you love to be outside. You have a little experience tutoring, and you can sing. You also have five younger brothers. You hope to get an interview for this job, but because it pays well, you are concerned that the competition will be tough.

2. Give an example of two steps you might take either to prepare for or to arrange an interview with someone at the camp.

_____

_____

3. Circle the letter of the answer that best describes an example of appropriate behavior *during* the interview. On the lines, explain why your answer is correct and the others are not.
   a. Arrive dressed in jeans, so the interviewer will know you are a relaxed person.
   b. Rehearse a few things to say, so you will feel prepared.
   c. Call every few days after the interview to find out who got the job.
   d. Give some background about your experience and ask questions about the position.

_____

_____

4. Give an example of an appropriate way to follow up after the interview.

_____

_____

5. When you are communicating with others, why is it important to know when to be serious and when to use humor?

_____

_____

Read the following scenario, and then answer questions 6 and 7.

> You are working on a video project with your classmate, Trisha. She is consistently late for video shoots, shows up unprepared, and leaves early. However, her ideas are creative, and she is a good actress and director. She senses that you are angry and disappointed. You are concerned that the project will not be finished on time, and you have asked her to meet with you to discuss your concerns.

6. Give an example of something you can do during your meeting with Trisha that will create an atmosphere of respect and enable you to finish the work on time.

_____

_____

7. Would you blame Trisha for her shortcomings during this meeting? Explain your answer.

_____

_____

Name _____

Read the following scenario. Then, answer questions 8–10.

> You are a member of a committee that is planning an Astronomy Day at your school. The group meets once a week to plan and discuss ideas about how to make the event a success.

8. Give an example of how committee members can participate in a group discussion by effectively communicating with others.

   _____

9. Choose one of the following roles of a group member—facilitator, recorder, or participant—and define his or her responsibility.

   _____

   _____

10. What should members of a committee do when they feel criticized by someone else in the group during a discussion?

   _____

   _____

11. Explain why having an agenda for a meeting is important.

   _____

   _____

12. a. Give an example of a step someone might take to achieve the personal goal of overcoming his or her fear of heights.

   _____

   b. Give an example of a step someone might take to achieve the professional goal of opening his or her own bakery.

   _____

13. Give an example of a step you could take to learn about a summer internship in a field you are interested in.

   _____

   _____

Refer to the following scenario to answer questions 14–17.

> Students and teachers—some of whom live several miles away from the high school—have to drive to school. There are not enough spaces in either the students' or the teachers' parking lot. There are several side streets near the high school, but the residents don't want people parking on their street all day. There are some local businesses near the school that have large parking lots.

14. Fill in the chart below to help arrive at a possible solution.

Problem:
Solution #1:
Solution #2:
People to Involve:

15. State the parking problem in a different way from what you did in the diagram. List two possible solutions to the problem, remembering to think creatively.

_____

_____

_____

_____

16. Write a reason for and a reason against each solution given in the preceding question.

_____

_____

_____

_____

17. Choose a solution from above, and explain why you think it is the best one.

_____

_____

_____

18. Circle the letter of the answer that represents the best example of time management. On the line, explain your answer.
    a. getting a good night's sleep
    b. eating a healthy breakfast every morning
    c. keeping a daily calendar
    d. expressing yourself in a logical manner

_____

19. Give an example of a school-related task that is part of your daily activities. Include how much time you usually spend on it.

_____

_____

20. Explain whether you think you have allowed enough time in your day for this task. If you have not allowed enough time, give an example of a change you could make.

_____

_____

_____

21. List five activities that you do each week, and rank them by number according to their importance (1 being most important and 5 being the least important).

_____

_____

_____

_____

_____

22. Read the chart below, which represents your hypothetical current income, expenses, and savings. Use the second chart to curtail some of your expenses so that you will be able to save an additional $20 each month, resulting in a total monthly savings of $50.

Activities	Monthly Income	Monthly Expenses	Monthly Savings
part-time job	$150.00		
movies		$30.00	
gifts		25.00	
books and CDs		25.00	
dinner out		40.00	
Totals		$120.00	$30.00

Activities	Monthly Income	Monthly Expenses	Monthly Savings
part-time			
movies			
gifts			
books and CDs			
dinner out			
Totals			

23. Circle the letter that represents a common, real-world application of mathematical skills. On the line, explain your answer.
    a. finding the square root of 125
    b. calculating the dimensions for a room you wish to carpet
    c. proofreading your work for mistakes
    d. sanding a piece of wood to prepare it for painting

    _____
    _____
    _____

24. Give an example of how adults use mathematics to help them to manage their money in their everyday lives.

    _____
    _____
    _____

25. Name one way in which the knowledge of word processing techniques—such as using different sizes and styles of fonts, boldface type, or italics—might be useful in a professional environment.

    _____

Answers

Key to Ability Levels: E = Easy; A = Average; C = Challenging

Chapter 1: The Writer in You (p. 3)

1. E   Writing is important because you will need to use it in your everyday life.
2. A   c. Using a variety of structures will make your writing flow.
3. C   *Voice* refers to qualities that set your writing apart from the work of others; *word choice* can determine whether a reader understands your ideas.
4. C   Keeping track of your ideas will assist you in choosing subject matter for writing.
5. E   d. A creative piece can be based on an idea on style from a poem collected in a style journal.
6. E   It will allow you to examine how your writing has developed and how it needs to be improved.
7. C   Students' answers should indicate their thoughts and feelings about the piece, and why they feel that way.
8. A   c. This is an example of an activity that you do before you write. The other answers are activities performed during or after writing.
9. E   If you find something that isn't working for you, go back to an earlier stage of the process. It is important to remember because it will allow you to review or reexamine your writing.
10. A   6, 3, 1, 2, 4, 5. This order indicates how one proceeds in the writing process in order to take an idea and turn it into a finished, written product.
11. A   Effective locations for writing should be free of outside distractions, well lit, and have all of the tools you need to write. Answers may include a library or a quiet room at home.
12. E   a. Working with others involves listening and can result in new ideas.
13. C   *Sample:* You want to encourage the creative process.
14. A   *Samples:*
    Collaborative Writing: A group works together to complete a project.
    Peer Reviewers: Having a peer read a draft will help the writer to catch mistakes and identify ideas that need further elaboration.
15. E   Publishing can build the writer's confidence in his or her abilities.
16. A   A student writer might publish in a school magazine or newspaper.
17. A   Asking questions about your writing successes and obstacles can help you grow as a writer.
18. A   a. The other answers will not help you evaluate the strengths and weaknesses of your work.

19. A   *Samples:*
    Defense lawyer: has to prepare documents for court, including a closing argument.
    Personal trainer: has to keep track of client's progress; has to advertise his or her business.
20. A   *Sample:* A politician might use his or her writing skills to create a persuasive speech.

Chapter 2: A Walk Through the Writing Process (p. 7)

1. E   Mode; Reflexive writing; Extensive writing
2. A   c, d, e, a, b
3. C   The diagram shows that writing is a recursive process.
4. C   Brainstorming helps you gather possible topics for writing.
5. A   A pentad helps to identify key elements of a topic.
6. A   Answers will vary based on the topic and the intended audience. Students should evaluate realistically how much the audience would know about the topic.
7. C   *Samples:*
    Peers: details that interest the writer's peer group
    Your teacher: details that explain the value of the hobby
    Other people: more complex details that such specialists would appreciate
8. C   *Sample:* One possible purpose is to share an insight about the positive aspects of having such a hobby.
9. C   Students' answers will vary. They should provide detailed answers to the questions asked in the cubing strategy.
    Sample: Cubing is useful for looking at a topic from a variety of perspectives.
10. A   A timeline generates information about when events occurred in a given time period.
11. C   A powerful lead grabs the readers' attention and invites them to continue reading.
12. A   *Samples:*
    Fact: Did you know that only three out of ten people can juggle?
    Description: Sometimes, when I look at the sky, I don't see clouds; I see three colored balls traveling in a vertical circle.
13. E   a. This answer sums up the sentences in the paragraph.
14. A   *Extension:* Now that I've prepared . . .
    Elaboration: Each time . . .
15. C   b. *Ratiocination* helps you remember to focus on one element of your writing at a time. Color coding is one way to use it.

16. A Sentence 2 and the phrase "even though his sister didn't start until she was six" should be crossed out. This information has nothing to do with Jason's talent as a pianist, which is the focus of the paragraph.

17. E *Samples:*
This accomplished musician began playing piano . . .
The youngster was playing difficult pieces . . .

18. A A peer reviewer can point out weaknesses in your paper that you might not have noticed.

19. A *Sample:* You might look in an encyclopedia or a hobby magazine.

20. C A rubric helps you to understand how your work is evaluated.

Chapter 3: Paragraphs and Compositions (p. 10)

1. A A paragraph consists of a group of sentences about a single idea, while a composition consists of a series of related paragraphs that focus on a single topic.

2. E A *topic sentence* directly states the paragraph's main idea; some paragraphs have implied main ideas.

3. A *Sample:* The library is a good source of free information resources.

4. C *Sample:* Place last sentence as first sentence; then place topic sentence at the end.

5. E Students' sentences should clearly support the topic sentence.

6. E Answer may contain examples of how good reading has led students to succeed, or it may contain information about how this fact has been proven.

7. A All sentences in the paragraph should support, explain, or develop the topic sentence.

8. E c. The thesis is the idea that the composition develops.

9. E b, d, a, c

10. A *Samples:* First, Then, For example, In addition, Afterwards, Finally

11. C Answer will include at least three transitions that logically connect directions.

12. A Introduction: presents thesis statement and the writer's attitude toward the topic
Body: series of paragraphs that support, explain, and elaborate on thesis
Conclusion: summarizes the main idea

13. C *Samples:*
Community service is part of being an adult, so high-school students should learn about it.
Students can learn to help others in easy and satisfying ways.
Students can gather new skills while they do community service.
High schools should include community service as part of their requirements; it teaches real-world skills and leads students to become contributing members of society.

14. C A topical paragraph is focused on one idea.
A functional paragraph can be used to arouse interest, create emphasis, make a transition, or indicate dialogue.

15. C *Sample:* Then, I was transported to a wonderland of dreams. I saw the fluffy bear from the story my mother had been reading. He was smiling at me with delight.

16. A a. They are especially useful if you have to present a large amount of information about one subject.

17. A Sentence variety expresses tone, creates atmosphere, and keeps readers interested.

18. A *Diction* refers to a writer's choice of words.

19. A *Samples:* Formal English avoids slang and contractions. It adheres to the rules of Standard English and grammar.

20. A a. Formal—You want to make a good impression.
b. Informal—Casual language is usually used when communicating with friends.
c. Formal—Indicates respect for a professional relationship.
d. Informal—This type of language might appeal to teens.

Chapter 4: Narration: Autobiographical Writing

Test 1 (p. 14)

1. E Students should choose a specific experience with a clear conflict. It should be narrow enough to cover in a short narrative.

2. E Students' answers will vary. They should include information that clearly supports the purpose of informing, entertaining, or re-creating.

3. E Responses should contain specific details that can be used in the narrative.

4. E Students should use vivid details to describe the main character.

5. E *Sample:* As I lay on the sandy beach, the sun slowly rose over the horizon.

6. E Students should write coherent, well-organized drafts.

7. E Students should add interesting dialogue that reveals a character's thoughts or emotions.

8. E Students should clearly address the emotional impact of their experience.

9. E Students should add a paragraph that changes the emphasis, adds description, or makes a transition.

10. E *Samples:*
It was clear that I was going to be late.
Trouble reared its ugly head.

11. E The rewritten sentence should convey the same idea but begin with a word other than *I*.

12. E except, their, accept, affect
Students should correct their errors.

13. E Students should correctly identify weaknesses in their drafts.

14. E Students should explain why each reader would have an interest in the topic.

15. E *Sample:* My attitude changed in that I became more aware of details that I had thought were unimportant.

Chapter 4: Narration: Autobiographical Writing
Test 2 (p. 17)
1. A *Sample:* the last day of school; the ending of a friendship
2. A *Sample:* peers; to share insights about how to deal with the loss of a friend
3. A Responses should contain specific details that can be used in the narrative.
4. A Students should use vivid details to describe the main character.
5. A The starting point should contain details that will grab the readers' interest.
6. A Students should write coherent, well-organized drafts.
7. A *Sample:* "What did I do to make you so angry?" I asked her.
8. A Students should clearly address the emotional impact of their experience.
9. A Students should draw a line between *pace* and *Daniel*.
   Students should add a paragraph that changes the emphasis, adds description, or makes a transition.
10. A changes/changed
   Students should identify and correct unintentional shifts in verb tense.
11. A Added transitions should clarify the connection between two ideas.
12. A *Corrections:* affected, there, too, accept
13. A Students should correctly identify weaknesses in their drafts.
14. A *Sample:* I might publish my narrative in the school literary magazine or in a local newspaper.
15. A *Sample:* It was difficult to revise, because there were details I had to leave out to stay focused on the main idea.

Chapter 4: Narration: Autobiographical Writing
Test 3 (p. 21)
1. C Students should clearly identify why the event has meaning for them.
2. C *Sample:* peers; to share a personal insight
3. C Students should explain why they remember the experience, who else is involved, and what changes and feelings evolved from the experience, for themselves or others.
4. C Students should use vivid details to describe the main character.
5. C Opening sentences should engage the reader with the most meaningful aspects of the experience.
6. C Students should write coherent, well-organized drafts.
7. C Students should select a detail that could be elaborated through dialogue, such as a personal or telephone conversation.
8. C Students should clearly address the emotional impact of their experience.

9. C *Sample:*
   I'll never forget the day the tree house burned down—it was traumatic. I felt that my secure world had been forever shaken.
   Students should add a paragraph that changes the emphasis, adds description, or makes a transition.
10. C *Samples:*
   The next morning, I awakened to . . .
   My father and brother were . . .
11. C Students should use transitions to connect their ideas more clearly.
12. C *Corrections:* too, accept, There
13. C Students should correctly identify weaknesses in their drafts.
14. C *Sample:* I might publish my narrative in a publication about fire safety or about childhood memories.
15. C *Sample:* I found the prewriting most challenging, because I had trouble narrowing my topic.

Chapter 5: Narration: Short Story
Test 1 (p. 24)
1. E Students should use clear and specific details to identify the six elements in their stories.
2. E *Sample:* My purpose is to entertain the audience. I can do this by adding lots of action.
3. E Students should carefully specify how they will achieve their plans.
4. E Answers will vary but should be ordered logically, according to the plot structure.
5. E Students should provide appropriate details to show how the conflict will build.
6. E Students should write coherent statements, well-thought-out extensions, and elaborations that contain specific details.
7. E Students should write coherent, well-organized drafts.
8. E Students should add a sentence that hints at an event to come.
9. E Paragraph 2 begins with the word "Are"; paragraph 3 begins with "Positive."
10. E Students should add functional paragraphs that emphasize a point or make a logical transition.
11. E *Sample:* John stared at the roadblock for a long time. While he wondered whether they would be able to drive around it, he concluded John was right.
   Students should vary their sentence beginnings and lengths.
12. E "Do you think we should ask the police for assistance?" Joe asked.
   After a moment's thought, Brian said, "We could try."
   "Anyway," Joe concluded, "we could give it a shot."
   Students should correct their errors.
13. E Students should correctly identify weaknesses in their drafts.
14. E *Sample:* I would add suspenseful music in the background.

15. E *Sample:* I learned that I have to work more on using details to flesh out my writing.

Chapter 5: Narration: Short Story
Test 2 (p. 28)
1. A Students should use clear and specific details to identify the six elements in their stories.
2. A *Sample:* I want my audience to feel the suspense, so I will use foreshadowing in my details and dialogue.
3. A Students should carefully specify how they will achieve their plans.
4. A Answers will vary but should be ordered logically, according to the plot structure.
5. A Students should provide appropriate details to show how the conflict will build.
6. A Students should write coherent statements, well thought-out extensions, and elaborations that contain specific details.
7. A Students should write coherent, well-organized drafts.
8. A *Sample:*
The door creaked open, and a shadow covered Juanita's face.
Students should add a sentence that hints at events to come.
9. A Paragraph 2 begins with "Do"; paragraph 3 begins with "I'm."
10. A Students should add functional paragraphs that add to the depth of description in their drafts.
11. A *Sample:* She was amidst a crowd of people who were all talking into their videophone wrist bands, paying no attention to her.
Students should vary their sentence lengths and beginnings.
12. A Juanita said that she felt tired.
"Oh, really?" Marcus asked. "And why is that?"
"I don't know," Juanita answered. "Maybe I'm getting a cold."
Students should correct their errors.
13. A Students should correctly identify weaknesses in their drafts.
14. A *Sample:* I would want to submit my story, because I think it's a good example of a mystery that challenges the reader.
15. A *Sample:* I would advise writers to describe their characters in depth so that readers can identify with them.

Chapter 5: Narration: Short Story
Test 3 (p. 32)
1. C Students should use clear and specific details to identify the six elements in their stories.
2. C *Sample:* I want my audience to see natural events from a fictional perspective.
Plan: To do this, I will make sure that connections between the fictional story and the natural event are clear, and I will use symbols to represent natural events.
3. C Students should carefully specify how they will achieve their plans.

4. C Answers will vary but should be ordered logically, according to the plot structure.
5. C Students should provide appropriate details to show how the conflict will build.
6. C *Samples:*
Statement: The captain was a difficult taskmaster.
Extension: He didn't give his underlings any room for error.
Elaboration: Once, the cook was forced to peel 100 potatoes because he unwittingly asked the captain for a shore leave.
7. C Students should write coherent, well-organized drafts.
8. C *Sample:* The captain hovered over him, grinning menacingly.
9. C Students should add functional paragraphs that emphasize a point or make a logical transition.
10. C *Sample:*
"How are you, Private Reynolds?" General Hayes asked.
"All fine, Sir," Private Reynolds replied. "And how are you, Sir?"
"Quite well, thank you," the General answered.
Students should correct their errors.
11. C Students should write a sentence of dialogue that conveys the nature of the character speaking.
12. C "Don't worry," the Captain said, "we'll get through this storm."
"How?" asked the first mate. "Our main sail is torn, and we're taking on water."
The Captain assured his crew that he would find a way to safely get them to land.
Students should identify and fix their errors.
13. C Students should correctly identify weaknesses in their drafts.
14. C *Sample:* Visual and sound effects should be appropriate to the story.
15. C *Sample:* I learned that I have a knack for making up imaginative stories.

Chapter 6: Description
Test 1 (p. 36)
1. E Students should create a sketch that evokes feelings and thoughts about the event.
2. E *Samples:* Peers; to relate your insights about the event or experience
3. E *Samples:*
Sight: Deep azure of the sky; Smell: the slight whiff of jasmine tingling my nose.
4. E Students should indicate how their writing will change based upon the point of view that they choose to use.
5. E *Sample:* I will relate a personal experience, so I will write my essay in the first person.
6. E Students should use material from their graphic organizers to write coherent, well-organized drafts.
7. E Students should write three descriptive sentences using a variety of senses.

8. E Students should clearly define the dominant impression and identify irrelevant details.

9. E First sentence should be underlined; "The sea gulls . . ." should be crossed out.

10. E *Samples:*
The players, all of them carrying their mitts, took . . .
My brother stood on his seat in order to get a glimpse of one of his favorite stars, Mickey Mantle.
Students should add appositives to their drafts.

11. E Added details should strengthen description.

12. E Appositive: Sue Grafton—no commas; Appositive phrase: a restaurant famous for its cheesecake—comma between "Lindy's" and "a," and between "cheesecake" and "in."

13. E Students should correctly identify weaknesses in their drafts.

14. E *Sample:* I could mention a famous painting of a similar scene.

15. E *Sample:* I would tell them to use as many sensory details as they can, to make the description more lively.

Chapter 6: Description
Test 2 (p. 39)

1. A Sketches should contain or suggest details that can be used in the description.

2. A Audience and purpose should be appropriate to topic.

3. A Sensory details listed should evoke the place to be described.

4. A Students should delineate the difference in how their writing will change based upon the point of view.

5. A *Sample:* I will relate a personal experience, so I will write my essay in the first person.

6. A Students should use materials from their graphic organizers to write coherent, well-organized drafts.

7. A Students' sentences should use highlighted words to further develop and support their observations or ideas.

8. A *Circled details:* oasis of calm, green canopy that shields me, soothes my jangled nerves;
Cross outs: These highways are usually packed with cars; Most of these cars emit a large amount of exhaust fumes.

9. A Students should clearly define the dominant impression and identify irrelevant details.

10. A *Sample:* The birds, brown and white Canadian geese, fly overhead. A squirrel, the one I feed every day, hunts for nuts near my feet. Wherever I look, the park, an apparently dormant place, is alive.

11. A Students should add a descriptive sentence that will convey additional information.

12. A Pearl S. Buck—essential; *Silent Spring*—nonessential; once a bestseller—nonessential—comma after "novel"; comma before "once" and after "bestseller"

13. A Students should correctly identify weaknesses in their drafts.

14. A *Samples:* A travel magazine, the local library newsletter

15. A *Sample:* It was useful in helping me to picture my topic so I could then describe it in words.

Chapter 6: Description
Test 3 (p. 42)

1. C Students' sketches should contain details they can use for description.

2. C *Sample:* Audience: My classmates
Purpose: to interest
Word choices: good listener; well-organized; hard-working; like Eleanor Roosevelt; mentor

3. C *Samples:* Sight: a patient smile; Hearing: a gentle voice

4. C Students should delineate the difference in how their writing will change based upon the point of view.

5. C *Sample:* first-person point of view; I want to provide personal insights about my favorite person.

6. C Students should write coherent, well-organized drafts using details from their graphic organizers.

7. C Students should write three descriptive sentences using a variety of senses.

8. C Topic sentence: My grandmother's ability to tell a good story reflected an innate gift; the sentence could be placed at the end of the paragraph; details will lead up to this conclusion, and the reader discovers the concept of her "gift" at the end.

9. C Sarah Billings, the youngest member of the staff, taught art at Stevens Elementary School.

10. C Revised words should better reflect the tone of student drafts.

11. C Students should add sentences that clearly support the dominant impression.

12. C Jane, my sister, is vacationing in Los Angeles. She intends to visit Magnificent Films Studios, the site where many of her favorite movies were made. When she returns, Jane plans to read the book *The Making of MFS.*
Students should correctly identify and fix wrong punctuation of appositives.

13. C Students should correctly identify weaknesses in their drafts.

14. C *Sample:* I might wish to add a photograph of my subject.

15. C *Sample:* It was useful in helping me to picture my topic so I could then describe it in words.

Chapter 7: Persuasion: Persuasive Speech
Test 1 (p. 46)

1. E *Sample:* A: Lengthening the school day will increase student achievement; 1: Students will spend more time on tasks; 2: Students will have more time to get individualized attention; B. Lengthening the school day will enable school officials to help students deal with social issues; 1: Officials may devote extra time to helping students and teachers deal with communication issues; 2: Students may receive additional time for peer counseling.
2. E *Sample:* General Purpose: To show why it's a good idea to lengthen the school day;
   Specific Purpose: Audience should support lengthening the school day, because it will benefit students academically, personally, and socially.
3. E *Sample:* Reasons to lengthen school day: More time for students to practice skills; Reasons against lengthening the school day: It will result in increased expenses for running schools.
4. E *Sample:* Lengthening the school day will result in a win-win situation for students, parents, and teachers.
5. E Students should write conclusions that impress the reader.
6. E Students should write coherent statements, well thought-out extensions, and elaborations that contain specific details.
7. E Students should use details from their graphic organizers to write coherent, well-organized drafts.
8. E Outlines should be well-organized and contain well-chosen details.
9. E . . . and took out the garbage
   . . . and education
10. E Students should be aware of, and eliminate, empty phrases and hedging words.
11. E Students should add sentences that will convey meaningful information.
12. E *Corrections:* accept, than, council's, effects Students should correct homonym errors.
13. E Students should correctly identify weaknesses in their drafts.
14. E *Sample:* students, teachers, or parents
15. E *Sample:* I learned that writing a strong appeal will get an audience's attention.

Chapter 7: Persuasion: Persuasive Speech
Test 2 (p. 49)

1. A Students should write outlines that narrow their topics to something they can write about in a few paragraphs.
2. A Students should identify the purpose of their speeches in a way that demonstrates their understanding.
3. A Students should be able to argue for and against their topics in an effective way.

4. A Students should write appeals that are ear-catching.
   Students should write conclusions that impress the reader.
5. A *Sample:* For example, if a teen works the evening shift at the local supermarket and the shift isn't over until 8:30, this person will have to quit his job because of the restrictions that the curfew imposes.
6. A Students should write coherent statements, well thought-out extensions, and elaborations that contain specific details.
7. A Students should write coherent, well-organized drafts using details from their graphic organizers.
8. A Students should carefully eliminate irrelevant sentences.
9. A *Sample:* They will be unable to work an evening job, study late at a friend's house, or participate in certain volunteer community services.
10. A Students should be aware of, and eliminate, empty phrases and hedging words.
11. A Students should add sentences that will convey meaningful information.
12. A *Corrections:* accept, their, affect, knew Students should correct homonym errors.
13. A Students should correctly identify weaknesses in their drafts.
14. A *Sample:* I would emphasize some of my key points—the inability to work late or study at a friend's house—by using a parallel structure.
15. A *Sample:* I learned that many teenagers are faced with conflicts about curfews.

Chapter 7: Persuasion: Persuasive Speech
Test 3 (p. 53)

1. C Students should write outlines that narrow their topics to something they can write about in a few paragraphs.
2. C Students should identify the purposes of their speeches in a way that demonstrates their understanding.
3. C Students should be able to argue for and against their topics in an effective way.
4. C Students should write appeals that are ear-catching.
   Students should write conclusions that impress the reader.
5. C *Sample:* Currently in our local elementary school, reading classes are being held in storerooms, because there is no other place to put them.
   The elaboration illustrates the point being made in paragraph.
6. C Students should write coherent statements, well thought-out extensions, and elaborations that contains specific details.
7. C Students should write coherent, well-organized drafts using details from their graphic organizers.
8. C Students should add parallelism that makes sense and adds to the force of the argument.

9. C *Lastly, as I said before, it is also true that, kind of, Needless to say, it seems that*
Students should be aware of, and eliminate, empty phrases and hedging words.

10. C *Samples:*
My little brother is a curious soul who wonders about everything that goes on around him.
Steven is quite assertive.
Despite losing the match, Jonathan is still optimistic about his chances in the next tournament, if his opponent is less determined.

11. C Students should add sentences that will convey more supporting information.

12. C *Corrections:* accept, than, than
Students should correct homonym errors.

13. C Students should correctly identify weaknesses in their drafts.

14. C *Samples:* Arguments and examples could be written more specifically. Language to be revised might include words that are more cumbersome to speak aloud.

15. C *Sample:* I discovered that using parallel phrases is an effective speaking device that compels the attention of my audience.

Chapter 8: Persuasion: Advertisement
Test 1 (p. 57)
1. E *Sample:* Brite toothpaste
2. E Audience: Children; ages 8–12; somewhat familiar; neutral; fun and excitement; kids who don't like to brush their teeth
3. E *Samples:*
What does it taste like?
What colors does it come in?
4. E *Sample:* Brite toothpaste brightens up bedtime
5. E *Sample:* percentage of children ages 8–12 who preferred the taste of Brite to other toothpastes; How clean and cavity-free toothpaste keeps teeth
6. E *Sample:* a dentist
7. E Students should write coherent, well-organized drafts.
8. E *Cross out:* Charlie was born . . .
Students should eliminate extraneous information from their drafts.
9. E Charlie's Chocolate Chip Cookies are the sweet treat. Try one, you'll see!
Buy Charlie's Chocolate Chip Cookies. They're the best!
In a recent taste test, four out of five people chose Charlies' Chocolate Chip Cookies. So will you.
Students should correct run-on sentences.
10. E *Samples:*
good = delicious
best = richest
moist = mouth-watering
Students should correctly identify and revise weak adjectives.
11. E Added sentences should effectively add appeal to students' advertisements.

12. E *Corrections:* 50th St.; 10th Ave.; Nov.
Students should correct their abbreviations.
13. E Students should correctly identify weaknesses in their drafts.
14. E *Sample:* I would post it near the local supermarket, to attract customers.
15. E *Sample:* I was more comfortable with the verbal aspects, since I don't draw very well.

Chapter 8: Persuasion: Advertisement
Test 2 (p. 60)
1. a *Sample:* Clean Scene
2. A *Samples:* adults
interested in clean kitchen floors
want good value for their money
3. A *Samples:* How is Clean Scene different from other cleaning products? Is Clean Scene safe to use on all types of floors? How much does Clean Scene cost?
4. A *Sample:* Try Clean Scene—It's the mean clean!
5. A *Sample:* statistics showing how well product works; number of people who have switched to this product
6. A *Sample:* a floor care expert; a parent who cleans the floor
7. A Students should write coherent, well-organized drafts.
8. A Clean Scene has been on the market for two months.
Students should eliminate extraneous information from their drafts.
9. A Use Clean Scene on any no-wax floor in your house. It will safely clean and polish your wood floor, too. Clean Scene is especially formulated not to scratch floor surfaces.
Students should correct run-ons.
10. A dirty/filthy
bad/tough
nice/fragrant
Students should correct weak adjectives.
11. A Students should add additional persuasive sentences.
12. A *Corrections:* Mar. 15th; 1st; 3rd
Students should correct their abbreviations.
13. A Students should correctly identify weaknesses in their drafts.
14. A *Sample:* near the supermarket or hardware store, where people buy cleaning supplies
15. A *Sample:* I was more comfortable with the visual, because I have a hard time making up slogans, and I can draw well.

Chapter 8: Persuasion: Advertisement
Test 3 (p. 63)
1. C *Sample:* South High basketball game
2. C *Sample:* Audience: Local community; parents and friends; newspaper reporters
3. C *Samples:* Who is involved in the game? Where will it be? When will it occur?
4. C *Sample:* Come to the championship game.
5. C *Sample:* Come see the game of the century!

6. C *Sample:* Win-loss records of teams; how many times each team has won a championship

7. C Students should write coherent, well-organized drafts.

8. C (4) Game time is 8:00 P.M. (1) Come and see the high-school basketball game of the century! (3) Watch these two 15–0 teams battle it out for the state championship! (5) Don't miss the action! (2) Century High takes on its rival, South High at the Town Arena.
Students should make their key points more prominent.

9. C *Cross out:* They have worked so hard to get to this game; South might win this one because they have a better defense. The sentences should be crossed out because they do not support the main idea of the advertisement.
Student revisions should increase prominence of at least one key point.

10. C Cheer your team to victory at the Town Arena. Tip-off is at 8:00 p.m. Watch the defending champ South High take on Century High for the state crown. It's sure to be a fight to the finish!
Students should fix run-ons in their drafts.

11. C Students should add additional persuasive sentences.

12. C *Corrections:* Wed., Jan. 12th, 1st
Students should correct their abbreviations.

13. C Students should correctly identify weaknesses in their drafts

14. C *Samples:* High-school cafeteria, bus stops, post office, all places where the local community members would go regularly.

15. C *Sample:* I realized that creating an attention-getting, persuasive advertisement requires a lot of attention to details.

Chapter 9: Exposition: Comparison-and-Contrast Essay

Test 1 (p. 67)

1. E *Sample:* Comparison between basketball and baseball: both use a round ball; both are team sports; both involve a coach; different numbers of players involved; different game objectives involved; different playing areas

2. E *Samples:*
explanation of the game
language that instructs but is fun

3. E *Samples:* Are there any similarities in the fitness preparation of the athletes? In what ways are the strategies of the sports different? How did each of the sports develop?

4. E Answers will vary but will include an alternation of the subjects being compared and contrasted. Example: I. Introduction; II. How Walking Increases Fitness; III. How Running Increases Fitness

5. E *Sample:*
Example: Players in both sports use weight training in their training regimens; they emphasize different areas of training.

6. E *Sample:* Statistics: 50% of basketball players suffer knee injuries, while only 20% of baseball players do.

7. E Students should write coherent, well-organized drafts.

8. E *Sample:* Runners are prone to more serious injuries than walkers. Students should rewrite topic sentences.

9. E Line should be drawn before the sentence beginning, "Walking is also . . ."
Students should explain how they will divide their paragraphs.

10. E Walking is a low-impact exercise that strengthens muscles.
Walking is a flexible form of exercise that can be adapted to suit your lifestyle.
Many people prefer walking to running, because they don't get injured as much when they walk.
Students should combine simple sentences.

11. E *Samples:* however, although

12. E *Corrections:* friends,
I run,
mind,
body,
Students should add commas as needed.

13. E Students should correctly identify weaknesses in their drafts.

14. E *Sample:* the school newspaper or the local sports section

15. E *Sample:* I learned that there were many more similarities than I had realized.

Chapter 9: Exposition: Comparison-and-Contrast Essay

Test 2 (p. 71)

1. A *Sample:* Both pens use ink cartridges; both are made of stainless steel; both pens can be monogrammed; Pen X costs twice as much as Pen Y; Pen X only comes in red, while Pen Y comes in different colors; Pen X is only used for calligraphy, while Pen Y is used for different purposes.

2. A *Sample:* Tone: persuasive; Details: should evaluate why and how Pen Y is superior (e.g., quality of writing; durability, versatility)

3. A *Sample:* How are the pens made? Why is Pen Y better for letter writing? What makes Pen X less durable?

4. A Answers will vary but will be organized according to the categories that will be used to compare and contrast the subjects.
Example: I. Durability; A. Pen X; B. Pen Y; II. Cost; A. Pen X; B. Pen Y

5. A *Sample:* Pen Y is more durable.

6. A *Sample:* In a study conducted by the manufacturer, it was found that Pen Y was 50% more likely not to crack in stress tests.

7. A Students should write coherent, well-organized drafts.
8. A *Sample:* You can save money and time if you wash your own car.
Students should improve at least one topic sentence.
9. A *Sample:* However, you need not simply dismiss the idea of having your car washed professionally. You may wish to take a look at its comparative benefits, even though it can be costly.
Students should write functional paragraphs.
10. A Line should be drawn between "purchased" and "However."
Students should recognize paragraphs that need to be broken.
11. A *Samples:*
Even though washing your car can be fun, it can also be time-consuming.
While many people prefer to wash their own cars, others would rather take their cars to a car wash.
Car washes are more expensive, because you are paying for a service.
Students should combine sentences in their drafts.
12. A *Corrections:* car, detergent, finish, job, use,
13. A Students should correctly identify weaknesses in their drafts.
14. A *Sample:* They would probably disagree, because most people won't take the time to wash their cars by hand.
15. A *Sample:* I would suggest that they do a chart first to make sure there is enough to write about on each subject.

Chapter 9: Exposition: Comparison-and-Contrast Essay
Test 3 (p. 75)
1. C *Sample:* video games vs. outdoor sports: both activities improve eye-hand coordination; both keep children interested; both can be enjoyed by a variety of people; one is played outside, the other inside; video games involve less physical exertion; outdoor sports involves less use of electronic equipment.
2. C *Sample:* unique connections between two apparently unlike ideas; quotes from authorities; examples to prove the points made
3. C *Sample:* What specific examples prove that these areas are similar? Are there any reasons that these areas are similar? Why should my view about these subjects change? Is there any statistical or historical proof for my ideas?
4. C Students may choose either form of organization, but they should be able to clearly justify their choice and demonstrate that it works well.

5. C *Samples:*
Example: The eye-hand coordination you use to play X video is similar to the eye-hand coordination you use when playing tennis.
Example: A higher percentage of girls play outdoor sports. A higher percentage of boys play video games.
Example: Video games have declined in popularity, as kids have started wanting to be healthier.
6. C *Sample:* A recent study confirmed that children are as likely to be entertained by outdoor sports as they are by indoor video games.
7. C Students should write coherent, well-organized drafts using information from their graphic organizers.
8. C *Samples:* Outdoor sports such as tennis or baseball require the player to evaluate the speed of the ball and decide when the racket or bat must be moved to strike it. Similarly, video-game players need to watch the screen in order to decide when to click the control panel in order to set into motion the action on the screen. No matter how it is developed, eye-hand coordination is an important skill for children to develop.
Students should improve the supporting sentences in their drafts.
9. C *Sample:* What is the "special language" used by jazz musicians? Like classical music, jazz has its own rhythms, its own words, and its own way of touching the soul.
Students should add functional paragraphs.
10. C *Samples:*
Both poetry and folk music may deal with real-world social or political issues
You take a job to earn money, but you choose a career to gain satisfaction.
Students should correctly combine two short sentences into one.
11. C *Sample:* Similarly, however, on the other hand
Students should add transitions to their drafts.
12. C *Corrections:* popularity,
no comma after listen
later,
13. C Students should correctly identify weaknesses in their drafts.
14. C Students may mention photographs, video clips, and audio recordings, among others.
15. C *Sample:* I learned that they are more similar than I had realized.

Chapter 10: Exposition: Cause-and-Effect Essay
Test 1 (p. 79)

1. E *Sample:* Center: Longer school day
   Subtopics: more time for instruction, greater opportunity to identify students at risk of failure, more money spent on education
   Subtopic: more time for instruction
2. E Audience: people interested in school policies
   Purpose: to inform
3. E *Samples:* statistics that illustrate effects of longer school day on learning; desire to increase test scores
4. E *Sample:* 1. Increased learning time for students; 2. Opportunity to introduce new academic programs; 3. Increased convenience for working parents.
5. E Students should mention a detail to which readers may relate.
6. E Students should share information that will allow readers to identify with the argument.
7. E Students should write coherent, well-organized drafts using material from the graphic organizer.
8. E Students should carefully check their organization and revise it if needed.
9. E *Samples:*
   however/in addition
   otherwise/as a result
   and/but
10. E *Samples:*
   Before computers were used in schools, many students wrote their essays by hand.
   The Internet is such a convenient source of information that many students have learned to use computers as research tools.
   Computers, which are the tools of the twenty-first century, will continue to influence the way that students learn in schools.
   Students should correct errors in the use of subordinate clauses.
11. E *Cross outs:* It seems; have tended to, rather
12. E *Samples*
   The word-processing programs in school, which were just purchased by the district, are easy to use.
   Students can use the library to do research on the computer, a tool that will help them immensely.
   The Internet, now in use all over the world, is an easy-to-use source of information.
   Students should add one nonessential expression to their drafts.
13. E Students should carefully evaluate their work for possible errors or changes.
14. E *Sample:* students who are having trouble in school and need tutoring time
15. E *Sample:* I discovered that there are many students who support this concept.

Chapter 10: Exposition: Cause-and-Effect Essay
Test 2 (p. 83)

1. A The general topic should lend itself to many possible subtopics. The subtopic should be one that can be covered in a short essay.
2. A The audience and purpose should be logically selected.
3. A Students should offer details that can support their purposes.
4. A Students should organize their drafts in a coherent manner.
5. A Students should mention a detail to which readers may relate.
6. A Students should share information that will affect readers' sympathies.
7. A Students should write coherent, well-organized drafts using material from the graphic organizer.
8. A *Samples:* People who learn skills such as auto repair have a better chance of landing a job and building a career. Many unskilled workers have difficulty finding jobs because they can offer nothing valuable to potential employers. Students should rewrite a paragraph to improve the flow from topic to last sentence.
9. A *Samples:*
   Therefore, there is a better chance . . .
   Moreover, specific workplace . . .
   Consequently, anyone who . . .
   Students should correct conjunction errors.
10. A *Samples:*
   Many unskilled workers have difficulty finding jobs because they can offer nothing valuable to potential employers.
   Not only is computer technology a growing field, but it is also spreading into all aspects of our lives.
   Vocational training can lead to high-paying jobs and worker satisfaction.
   Students should add subordinate clauses to their drafts.
11. A *Cross outs:* sort of, rather, kind of
   Students should cite unnecessary qualfiers.
12. A Paul has decided to attend Teterboro State, the aviation school.
   Alexis Herman, Secretary of Labor, has announced a new government initiative aimed at funding vocational training programs.
   Students should rewrite two sentences so that they have nonessential expressions.
13. A Students should carefully evaluate their work for possible errors or changes.
14. A *Sample:* Since many of them know about technology, I would expect them to agree with the positive aspects of my essay.
15. A *Sample:* I would tell him or her to list many effects for the cause, so that there are enough details.

Chapter 10: Exposition: Cause-and-Effect Essay
Test 3 (p. 87)

1. C *Sample:* Center: High-speed trains
   Subtopics: Changed commuting habits; loss of jobs; more rootlessness as a society; less pollution
   Subtopic: Changed commuting habits

2. C *Samples:*
   Audience: Peers
   Purpose: To predict

3. C *Sample:* Present examples and statistics, such as fewer cars on road, less of a local flavor in towns and cities, greater opportunity to visit distant places

4. C Students should organize their drafts in a coherent manner and justify their choices.

5. C Students should mention a detail to which readers may relate.

6. C Students should share information with which readers may sympathize.

7. C Students should write coherent, well-organized drafts using material from graphic organizers.

8. C Students should carefully check their organization and change it, if needed, and explain why.

9. C Space travel will be possible in the future, but it will be expensive.
   There have been many advances in space technology, and these advances can be used to refine space travel.
   Today, it takes approximately four years for a spaceship to travel to Mars; however, in fifty years that travel time may be cut in half.
   Students should add conjunctions to their drafts.

10. C *Samples:*
    Topic sentence: Telecommuting isn't science fiction any more.
    Concluding sentence: Thus, telecommuting enables the employee to do the same type of work from the comfort of his home.
    Students should fix errors in paragraph flow.

11. C *Samples:*
    . . . life, though in other ways life will not change at all.
    . . . disadvantage, because they have not trained in new technologies.
    . . . activities, which will use more and more electronic gadgetry
    Students should explain how additions elaborate ideas. The students should enrich sentences by adding subordinate clauses.

12. C *Corrections:* Technology, decade, access, net," called,
    Students should correct comma errors.

13. C Students should carefully evaluate their work for possible errors or changes.

14. C *Samples:* Student anthology, school newspaper
    Others might be thinking about these issues.

15. C *Sample:* I would tell her to eliminate vague ideas that do not directly support her purpose, add more specific present examples that point to future trends, and convey a purposeful tone.

Chapter 11: Exposition: Problem-and-Solution Essay
Test 1 (p. 91)

1. E The general topic should lend itself to more specific topics. The narrowed topic should be one that can be covered in a short essay.

2. E The purpose for writing is for students to explain to a specific audience their ideas for solving a problem.

3. E Students should offer details that support possible problems and solutions.

4. E Students should organize their drafts in a coherent manner.

5. E Students should mention a detail to which readers can relate.

6. E Students should share information that will affect readers positively.

7. E Students should write coherent, well-organized drafts.

8. E *Sample:* Finding a college to suit your academic and personal needs is easy if you make your inquiries in an organized manner.
   Students should improve one of their topic sentences.

9. E *Sample:* Changing the oil in a car is a fairly straightforward procedure, as long as you follow all of the steps involved. Nevertheless, there will always be someone who doesn't follow these steps carefully. The person's carelessness can result in disaster.
   Students should rewrite long sentences as shorter pairs of sentences.

10. E Talking to your parents is one way to solve the problem.
    Following directions is important in baking a souffle.
    It is important to eliminate any outside issues when discussing your request.
    Students should rewrite sentences to include subject complements.

11. E Redundant words: first, aloud, on all sides
    Students should eliminate redundancies in their essays.

12. E *Corrections:* greenish-blue, ex-football, graduation—which was held outdoors—
    Students should add hyphens or dashes to their drafts where needed.

13. E Students should use the rubric to identify and correct their errors.

14. E *Samples:* The school newspaper or the community newspaper would help me to reach a local audience.

15. E *Sample:* I learned that I needed to do a lot of revision to create more sentence variety.

Chapter 11: Exposition: Problem-and-Solution Essay

Test 2 (p. 95)

1. A   The general topic should lend itself to more specific topics. The narrowed topic should be one that can be covered in a short essay.
2. A   The purpose for writing is for students to explain to a specific audience their ideas for solving a problem.
3. A   Students should offer details that support possible problems and solutions.
4. A   Students should organize their drafts in a coherent manner.
5. A   Students should mention a detail to which readers can relate.
6. A   Students should share information that will affect readers favorably.
7. A   Students should write coherent, well-organized drafts.
8. A   *Sample:* Finding a college that suits your academic needs is easy if you plan the steps that you need to take.
       Students should improve their topic sentences.
9. A   *Sample:* Place the following as the first sentence: Here are some important steps to follow when selecting a college.
10. A   *Samples:*
       It is important that parents talk to their children before setting a curfew.
       Designating a quiet place to study is one way that students can focus on their work.
       A balanced diet is the key to better health.
       Students should rewrite topic sentences to include subject complements.
11. A   Redundant words: first, different, unknown
       Students should eliminate redundancies in their essays.
12. A   *Corrections:* self-addressed, all-day, kitchen—no, it's over here.
13. A   Students should use the rubric to identify and correct their errors.
14. A   *Sample:* I would publish it in the school newspaper or post it on a bulletin board.
15. A   *Sample:* It helped me to realize that my topic was too complex to cover in a short essay.

Chapter 11: Exposition: Problem-and-Solution Essay

Test 3 (p. 99)

1. C   *Samples:*
       Center circle: traffic congestion
       Specific topics: stress; air pollution; car pooling; public transportation; walking
       Narrowed topic: air pollution
2. C   *Sample:* My audience is the town council because the council members might be able to control traffic congestion, a major cause of air pollution.
       Details: evidence of air pollution, possible solutions to problem, personal experiences

3. C   *Samples:*
       Problem: traffic congestion causes air pollution
       Solutions: encourage carpooling; make public transportation more available; create bicycle lanes
4. C   Students should organize their drafts in a coherent manner and indicate their reasons for the type of organization they chose.
5. C   *Sample:* Illnesses caused by air pollution are serious issues that affect the health of community members and can result in hospitalization or even death.
       Historical example: An example showing how air pollution in areas such as Mexico City or Los Angeles has resulted in increased numbers of pulmonary illnesses.
6. C   Students should show how their choices will help to accomplish the purpose of their essay.
7. C   Students should write coherent, well-organized drafts.
8. C   *Underline:* What should we do about it? . . . released into the air.
       Sample: This imbalance may be corrected by devoting a separate paragraph to possible solutions.
       Students should balance the subjects in their drafts.
9. C   *Sample:* Carpooling is an effective way to reduce the level of air pollution in our city. It may be placed at the beginning of the paragraph to focus readers on this solution.
       Students should rearrange topic sentences as needed.
10. C   *Samples:*
       Walking is one way to save energy and money.
       Muscles are strengthened by walking.
       On the other hand, commuting to work is stressful.
       Students should add subject complements to their drafts.
11. C   Redundant words: free, back, unknown
       Students should eliminate redundancies in their drafts.
12. C   *Corrections:* ex-army, all-day, was—can you believe it?—
       Students should check their drafts and add hyphens or dashes as needed.
13. C   Students should use the rubric to identify and correct errors in their drafts.
14. C   *Sample:* I would want to encourage people in my town to think about this problem and to take it seriously.
15. C   *Sample:* I tried to come up with statistics to support the seriousness of the problem, and I was successful in finding several of them.

Chapter 12: Research: Documented Essay

Test 1 (p. 104)

1. E   Students should effectively model the looping process to narrow the topic to one that can be covered in a short essay.

2. E *Sample:* Sarah's purpose is to garner support for the efforts aimed at saving the tiger. She should include specific examples of abuses and efforts aimed at saving the tiger.

3. E Sarah has used the Internet, newspaper articles, and a multimedia encyclopedia.

4. E *Sample:*
   I. Definition of endangered species
   1. Natural rate of extinction and how rate of extinction differs from natural extinction rate
   2. How the tiger has become extinct
   3. Efforts made to save the tiger
   Conclusion: Why it is important to continue efforts to save the tiger

5. E *Sample:* Sarah might use note card #2 because it explains why tigers are endangered species.

6. E *Samples:*
   Sarah might elaborate on the use of tiger bones in medicine and on other uses of the tiger in worldwide markets.

7. E For example, elephants are in danger of extinction . . . and that's why I'm writing about the tiger

8. E Even though there are efforts . . .
   This sentence would be more effective if it were the first sentence. This would help the reader to focus on the extinction of tigers, rather than on extinction in general.

9. E *Sample:*
   Repeated word: extinction
   Rewrite: . . . tigers are currently being hunted to the point of extermination. (other synonyms: dying out, destruction)

10. E *They* have been hunted . . .
    . . . but *their* efforts have been only . . .

11. E *Sample:* Sarah should adopt a serious tone. She might use words such as *stalked, crisis,* and *prey.*

12. E *Sample:* The detail about "background rates" should be cited, because it represents a term with which readers would be unfamiliar (note card #1).

13. E *Sample: The New York Times* reports that between 1998 and 2000, 66 tigers were poached. (note card #4).

14. E *Sample:* She could deliver a speech and use the visual aid of a chart depicting the tiger's rate of extinction.

15. E *Sample:* I learned that the Internet is useful for accessing information from encyclopedias.

Chapter 12: **Research: Documented Essay**
Test 2 (p. 107)
1. A Students should effectively model the looping process to narrow the topic to one that can be covered in a short essay.

2. A *Sample:* John's purpose might be to inform readers about Shakespeare's early life. He should include specific details about Shakespeare's childhood and schooling.

3. A *Samples:*
   To examine Shakespeare's early life, John might use an encyclopedia.
   To determine whether any influences on his writing can be found, John might use a nonfiction reference book.
   To find examples that indicate ideas or themes in his later works, John might interview a scholar in the field.

4. A "Although William Shakespeare . . ." gives the essay a specific focus.

5. A *Sample:* John might explore Shakespeare's schooling in a paragraph block.

6. A *Sample:* He studied for nine hours a day, especially Latin.

7. A *Cross outs:* Its educator was paid . . . This detail does not teach the reader anything about Shakespeare.

8. A *Sample:* Shakespeare's early life was pleasant and undistinguished.
   The sentence should be first, to introduce the other ideas.

9. A *Samples:* Shakespeare's father, John, was a collector of fines for the town of Stratford-on-Avon, and he was regarded as part of the well-to-do class.
   Shakespeare attended the prestigious Stratford Grammar School at the age of seven, but he does not appear to have continued his education beyond that point.

10. A His father, John . . .
    He does not appear . . .

11. A John could add that Shakespeare's father was philanthropic by explaining that he gave aid to plague victims.

12. A "Capital burgesses" should be a direct quotation, because it is probably an unfamiliar term. (note card #1).

13. A The description of Stratford as a corporate borough could be paraphrased (note card #2).

14. A *Sample:* It could be classified as a literary biography or as an essay on a famous playwright.

15. A *Sample:* I did not know that details about Shakespeare's early marriage years were unknown.

Chapter 12: **Research: Documented Essay**
Test 3 (p. 110)
1. C Students should effectively model the looping process to narrow the topic to one that can be covered in a short essay.

2. C *Sample:*
   Topic: Miro's role in Surrealist movement
   Question: What other examples of Miro's interpretation of surrealist concepts can you discuss?
   Plan: Examine biographies of Miro

3. C *Samples:* Monica might consult art magazines because they will give additional insights into Miro's work.

4. C   *Sample:* Miro is a good example of the Surrealistic influence on art. This statement is a good main idea because Miro is a major figure in the Surrealist movement.

5. C   *Sample:* Miro's exposure to Surrealism could be explored through an examination of a few of his works.

6. C   *Sample:* Note card #3 refers to Miro's feeling liberated by Surrealism. This would be an important aspect to include because it explains why he believed in Surrealism.

7. C   *Sample:* Miro's flexibility in his approach to painting shows his growth as an artist. The sentence should be placed first, because the rest of the paragraph supports it.

8. C   The last sentence could be eliminated, because it is more focused on one specific painting than on Miro's artistic growth.

9. C   *Samples:*
free/uninhibited
upset/felt restrained; disturbed

10. C   The connotation of these words is more formal than that of the words they replaced. A formal tone is appropriate for this topic.

11. C   *Sample:* The basis for Surrealism was a belief that dreams produced useful information (note card #1).

12. C   *Sample:* The quote from note card #3 can be inserted after the second sentence, enclosed in quotations.

13. C   A sentence about other artists could be paraphrased (note cards #1 and #2), since this information would not need a citation, as it is generally available to the reader.

14. C   *Sample:* An art history teacher would appreciate a student's perspective on a great artist.

15. C   *Sample:* I would probably focus more on individual paintings and try to trace the Surrealist movement through more of Miro's actual works.

Chapter 13: Research: Research Paper
Test 1 (p. 113)

1. E   Students should effectively use a web to narrow the topic to one that can be covered in a short essay.

2. E   *Samples:* Frank should use colorful examples, stick to major historical events and people, and define any special baseball terms.

3. E   *Sample:* What I want to find out: Information about college baseball in 18th–19th centuries
Possible sources: book about baseball history and famous baseball heroes; biographies of baseball players

4. E   *Underline:* Baseball is an American sport . . .

5. E   He should use chronological order, because there is a time sequence to his information.

6. E   *Sample:* I. Rounders; A. Origins; B. Similarities to baseball (Doubleday myth); II. College baseball A. Princeton B. North Carolina; III. Rules A. Knickerbocker rules B. Examples

7. E   *Underline:* When was rounders invented?; How did rounders make its way to the U.S? Answering these questions will complete the information about the sport, and explain how it became a precursor to baseball.

8. E   This sentence is a restatement.

9. E   *Sample:*
Question: Where did our national pasttime originate?
Answer: Baseball originated not in America, but in England!

10. E   *Samples:* Baseball appears to have originated from rounders, an English game that has many similarities to modern baseball. Rounders was played on a diamond-shaped infield with a base at each corner. The batter was pitched a ball, and if he hit the ball through or over the infield, he could run.

11. E   *Sample:* Make the second sentence the first sentence, because it introduces the rest of the paragraph.

12. E   "The ancestor . . . . theory." The quotation is less than 4 lines long, so it should not be set as a block quotation.

13. E   . . . theory" (*Encyclopedia Britannica*, 160).

14. E   *Sample:* Frank could use a videotape of an exciting moment from a baseball game (from either a modern or early baseball film).

15. E   *Sample:* I thought the myth about Doubleday was true.

Chapter 13: Research: Research Paper
Test 2 (p. 117)

1. A   Students should effectively use a web to narrow the topic to one that can be covered in a short essay.

2. A   *Samples:*
What I want to find out: How did the public initially react to Picasso's cubist paintings?
Possible resources: Biographies about Picasso's professional life

3. A   *Sample:* Elizabeth might interview a professor of art history who specializes in Picasso's art.

4. A   *Sample:* Although Picasso had painted in various artistic styles as a young boy, he is probably best known for his cubist paintings and is credited as one of the founders of the cubist movement.

5. A   *Sample:* Elizabeth might use cause-and-effect organization to show why Picasso gravitated to cubism and what the result was

6. A   *Sample:* I. Early influence. A. Art School. B. Paris II. Later Paris work A. 1907–1912 B. 1913–1920

7. A *Sample: Les Demoiselles Davignon* is an early example of Picasso's cubist work (note card #3).

8. A *Sample:*
Question: What was the basis of the cubist movement, and how was Picasso involved in it?
Answer: He was part of an intellectual revolt against the art of the time.
(The above approach focuses the paragraph more on cubism, with the idea that Picasso's switch to surrealism would be discussed in a later paragraph.)

9. A *Samples:*
At the turn of the century, Picasso developed the idea of cubism.
His transition to cubism was exemplified in his work from that period, and he continued to work in it for several years, when he switched to a more surrealistic style.

10. A *Samples:* Eliminate both uses of "you could tell."
Either use "one" instead of "you could tell," or rewrite the sentences as follows:
He switched to . . .
At that point . . . he switched to . . .

11. A *Sample:* The sentence "It was the turn of the century" should be moved to the beginning of the paragraph to show the time period more clearly.

12. A The quotation is less than four lines long, so Elizabeth should enclose it in quotation marks, followed by a parenthetical citation.

13. A *Sample:* Picasso expressed his political feelings through his artwork (note card #4).

14. A *Sample:* Elizabeth might choose a Web site that discusses the work of major artists.

15. A *Sample:* She has some information about Picasso's early life that does not seem to connect with the other information she gathered. I would leave that information out.

Chapter 13: Research: Research Paper
Test 3 (p. 120)

1. C Students should effectively use a web to narrow the topic to one that can be covered in a short essay.

2. C *Sample:* What I want to find out: Events in World War II that led to Cold War; the relationship between the U.S. and its allies; the political and military climate in the U.S.S.R.
Possible sources: Web sites and nonfiction books about the Cold War and about the history of the U.S.S.R.

3. C *Sample:* Harrison might use historical treatises on the subject.

4. C *Sample:* While the Cold War Period lasted from 1945 to 1989, the factors that led to it began far earlier.

5. C *Sample:* Harrison might use cause-and-effect organization because he is examining the reasons (causes) of the Cold War (effect).

6. C *Sample:* I. World War A. Eastern Front issue B. Hostility between allies and U.S.S.R. C. Impact on Cold War II. Grand Alliance III. Poland issue

7. C The quotation about "a war without a war" could be used (note card #1).

8. C *Sample:* Question: Where does the term "Cold War" come from, and what does it mean? Answer: The Cold War is a term coined by journalist Walter Lipman in 1947 to describe the relationship between the U.S. and U.S.S.R. to describe their relationship just after World War II. Lipman used it to mean that the relationship between the two countries had deteriorated to the point of war without actually waging one.

9. C *Samples:*
The term "Cold War" was coined by Walter Lipman in 1947.
It refers to the relationship between the U.S.S.R. and the U.S. and its allies. The Cold War existed from the late 1940's to the 1980's, when the Berlin Wall fell.

10. C *Sample:* Today, not everyone is familiar with the longstanding hostility that existed between the U.S. and the U.S.S.R. after World War II.
This sentence should be placed first to introduce the rest of the information in the paragraph.

11. C The term "Cold War" is in quotations, so it should be cited.

12. C Direct quotation (from note card #2): "In 1918 . . ."
It should be placed after the first sentence, to help illustrate the point.

13. C Harrison should place the parenthetical citation at end of the quotation, outside quotation marks.

14. C *Sample:* Harrison might use a timeline illustrating key dates and events.

15. C *Sample:* He might try interviewing some people who lived through the Cold War, to get a primary source.

Chapter 14: Response to Literature
Test 1 (p. 123)

1. E Students should effectively model the looping process to narrow the topic to one that can be covered in a short essay.

2. E *Samples:*
The teacher would expect to see clear, well-supported responses.
The writing style should be formal.

3. E The hexagonal chart should show concrete evidence of how the student is carefully analyzing the poem.

4. E The outline should organize ideas that culminate in a strong conclusion.

5. E *Sample:* "How do I love thee? Let me count the ways" and "I love thee to the depth and breadth and height/My soul can reach . . ." express the idea that the poet has chosen to structure the poem as the answer to a question.

6. A *Sample:* The tone is strong, romantic, and devoted: "I love thee with the breath, / Smiles, tears, of all my life!"

7. E Students should write coherent, well-organized drafts using material from the graphic organizer.

8. E The most important idea should be clearly identified.

9. E *Underline:* I especially enjoy the symmetry of sonnets. Students should eliminate digressions from their drafts.

10. E *Corrections:* most, more
Students should correct the use of comparatives and superlatives in their drafts.

11. E *Samples:* short/brief; interesting/ insightful; normal/commonplace; new/ novel
Students should improve their word choices.

12. E *Romeo and Juliet; Henry IV;* "When You Are Old"
Students should correct errors in the use of underlining and quotation marks in their drafts.

13. E Students should carefully evaluate their work for possible errors or changes.

14. E *Sample:* They would probably think that my ideas about how Barrett Browning was able to express her love was most important.

15. E *Sample:* The aspects relating to religion and death became clearer.

Chapter 14: Response to Literature
Test 2 (p. 127)

1. A Students should effectively model the looping process to narrow the topic to one that can be covered in a short essay.

2. A *Samples:*
Students would expect to see clear, well-supported responses.
The writing style should be formal.

3. A The hexagonal chart should show concrete evidence of how the student is carefully analyzing the poem.

4. A The outline should organize ideas that culminate in a strong conclusion.

5. A *Samples:*
"Death be not proud" supports the point that Donne is telling death that it should not be overconfident about its impact on humans.
"We wake eternally" supports the point that Donne believes in eternal life after death; therefore, eternity defeats death.

6. A *Samples:*
The context for "Death be not proud" is that we usually think of death as all-powerful.
The context for "We wake eternally" is that it refers to heaven or eternal life.

7. A Students should write coherent, well-organized drafts using material from the graphic organizer.

8. A *Underline:* The rose represents . . . (This symbol has nothing to do with the specific encounter.)
Students should eliminate digressions from their drafts.

9. A *Comparison:* three women/Mattie.
Corrections: strongest, oldest, most
Students should correct the use of comparatives and superlatives in their drafts.

10. A *Samples:* good/uplifting; hard/complex; rough/painful
Students should improve their word choices.

11. A *Sample:* Does my essay use Nestorian organization?

12. A *Death of a Salesman;* "The Necklace" "Leave It to Beaver"
Students should correct errors in the use of underlining and quotation marks in their drafts.

13. A Students should carefully evaluate their work for possible errors or changes.

14. A *Sample:* I would classify it as an analysis of how the poet expresses his ideas about death.

15. A *Sample:* It became clearer to me that Donne's decision to address Death directly made the poem even more powerful.

Chapter 14: Response to Literature
Test 3 (p. 131)

1. C Students should effectively use the looping process to narrow the topic to one that can be covered in a short essay.

2. C *Samples:* Audience: Peer response group; they want to evaluate the quality of my final product.
I would use formal language and carefully check grammar and puncuation.

3. C *Sample:* Similarities of works should be placed in intersecting area; differences should be placed in separate portions of circles.

4. C The outline should organize ideas that culminate in a strong conclusion.

5. C *Samples:*
"To an Athlete": "Smart lad, to slip betimes away"
"Holy Sonnet 10": "We wake eternally"
These quotations elaborate on the idea of escaping, or rising above, matters that only seem important (such as glory or death).

6. C "Smart lad": The context is that the runner has escaped competition.
"We wake eternally": The context is Donne's view of life after death as new life, not extinction.

7. C Students should write coherent, well-organized drafts using material from the graphic organizers.

8. C The most important idea should be clearly identified.

9. C Students should revise digressions from their drafts so that they clearly support the logic of the drafts.

10. C *Sample:* John is <u>more</u> qualified for the head counselor position. He has <u>more</u> experience in the daily operations of the camp than Maragaret. Even though Margaret has experience working with children, John is <u>better</u> certified to work at the camp and thus would probably be the <u>wiser</u> choice. Students should correct the use of comparatives and superlatives in their drafts.

11. C *Sample:* I will need to reorganize my ideas so that the most important idea is in the conclusion.

12. C <u>The Bean Trees</u>; "Soundness of Mind and Freedom of Will", "Dare's Gift"; <u>The Book of Southern Short Stories</u>; <u>Inherit the Wind</u>;
Students should correct errors in the use of underlining and quotation marks in their drafts.

13. C Students should carefully evaluate their work for possible errors or changes.

14. C *Sample:* I would discuss how death is viewed in each poem, and how the concept of victory differs in each poem.

15. C *Sample:* I found that I was able to find many more thematic similarities than I had anticipated.

Chapter 15: Writing for Assessment
Test 1 (p. 136)
1. E Argue for or against
2. E *Sample:* School officials should not be allowed to enforce a stricter dress code.
3. E *Sample:*
Audience: Teachers
Purpose: to persuade
4. E The organizational structure should be logically connected to the purpose of the essay.
5. E Students should choose details that support their points.
6. E Students should choose details that provide solid illustration for their points.
7. E Students should write coherent, well-organized drafts.
8. E *Sample:* Is community service a good idea? I think so.
Students should rewrite their first sentences.
9. E *Cross out:* I once volunteered . . .
Students should delete sentences that detract from the unity of their paragraphs.
10. E *Cross outs:* promotes, do, are, bother
Students should check verb tenses in their drafts.
11. E *Samples:* Similarly, Therefore
Students should add logical transitions to their drafts.
12. E *Corrections:* It's, hear, they're, their
13. E Students should carefully evaluate their work for possible errors or changes.
14. E *Sample:* It will help me understand some of the challenges I face in my writing, especially when I am writing for assessment purposes.

15. E *Sample:* I am satisfied, because the topic is one that is under debate at my high school.

Chapter 15: Writing for Assessment
Test 2 (p. 139)
1. A *Sample:* Examine the effects
2. A *Sample:* Speaking a second language will open more career paths to you.
3. A *Samples:*
Audience: peers
Purpose: to inform
4. A The organizational structure should support the purpose of the essay.
5. A Students should choose details that solidly support their points.
6. A Students should choose details that provide solid explantations for their points.
7. A Students should write coherent, well-organized drafts.
8. A *Sample:* Limiting the working hours of teenagers would effectively limit their growth as young adults.
Students should improve their opening sentences.
9. A *Sample:* All of these reasons emphasize the need for teenagers to develop responsibility and independence as they make their transition into the adult world.
Students should add transitional sentences to their essay introductions.
10. A I know that I . . .
Students should delete any sentences from their writing that detracts for the unity.
11. A will lose/lose
have gained/gain
lost/lose
Students should correct errors in verb tense in their drafts.
12. A *Corrections:* hear, its, effects
Students should correct errors in homophones in their drafts.
13. A Students should carefully evaluate their work for possible errors or changes.
14. A *Sample:* My guidance counselor would probably say that it is a good example of my writing, because I have tried to use details to support all of my points.
15. A *Sample:* I found revising most useful, because I changed my opening sentence to make it more interesting.

Chapter 15: Writing for Assessment
Test 3 (p. 142)
1. C *Samples:* analyze, examine, describe
2. C *Sample:* Visiting Mexico always brings back memories of my grandfather.
3. C *Samples:*
Audience: peers
Purpose: to inform or entertain
4. C The organizational structure should be logically connected to the purpose of the essay, and the students should explain their choices.
5. C Students should choose details that will support their points.

6. C Students should appropriately justify their choices of elaboration.
7. C Students should write coherent, well-organized drafts.
8. C Students should change their opening sentences to make them more compelling; they should write effective transitional sentences; and they should write strong concluding sentences.
9. C Students should analyze their drafts and eliminate or revise sentences that do not support the coherence of their drafts.
10. C Students should examine the verb tenses in their drafts, make them consistent, and justify their choices of verb tense.
11. C *Samples:*
Consequently, I always go there . . .
First, we walked . . .
Students should add transitions to their drafts.
12. C *Corrections:* There, sights, seen, heard, where
Students should correct homophones in their drafts.
13. C Students should carefully evaluate their work for possible errors or changes.
14. C *Sample:* This is a good example of a descriptive essay. I would save it to remind me to use extensive details in my writing. It represents one of my more skillfully written essays, because I am not as good at writing persuasive or cause-and-effect essays.
15. C *Sample:* I found revising useful, because I needed more transitions to emphasize the order in which events occurred.

Chapter 16: Workplace Writing (p. 145)
1. E c. A letter to the editor is fact-based and utilizes a structured format to communicate information; all other examples are of personal writing.
2. E *Samples:*
Presents a core message; communicates essential details; is neatly and effectively organized; is free from errors in grammar, spelling, punctuation.
3. C It must communicate information in a format that is appropriate for busy people to be able to read quickly.
4. A Business letters can communicate to people outside of the office; memos are intended for interoffice communication.
5. C a. This is an accepted salutation for a business letter; it is formally written.
6. C *Sample:* I believe that I possess the necessary qualifications for the position of research assistant at your firm. I have a strong school record, and varied work experience, from which I have developed excellent research skills.
7. A b. This answer contains the exact, factual information needed to explain a customer's dissatisfaction with a product.
8. E c. This is the intended audience, because a memo is circulated within an organization.

9. A Drafting; Revising; Publishing/Presenting; Prewriting; Editing/Proofreading.
Prewriting; Drafting; Revising; Editing/Proofreading; Publishing/Presenting.
10. A *Sample:* TO: Employees of Safewell, Inc.
FROM: J. Doe, Vice President of Human Resources
DATE: 9/25/01
RE: New Vacation Policy
11. C *Sample:* RE: Upgrading Computer Skills
12. C *Sample:* to show that you are professional, serious, and polished
13. A *Sample:* Sept. 1995–Oct. 1997: Project Manager, Rite-Way Advertising. Supervised projects to deadlines; Managed customer satisfaction issues. Skills: Writing and idea generation.
14. C *Sample:* Use action words to effectively describe your job responsiblities in a positive way.
15. A It is easier for a prospective employer to look for specific information about a candidate's qualifications.
16. C *Sample:* dates of employment or education; job descriptions that list skills I learned
17. E It tells what the message is about and gives other important information.
18. E It will ensure that the addressee receives the fax transmission.
19. E b. This specific information must be recorded for organizations like the post office so that mail is properly forwarded. The other answers do not require an application.
20. C Students should create a job application that has detailed, concise information.

Grammar, Usage, and Mechanics: Cumulative Diagnostic Test (p. 151)

The numbers in brackets indicate the chapter and section of the skills being tested.
1. A adverb/adjective/preposition [17.3, 17.4]
2. E verb/adjective [17.2, 17.3]
3. A noun/preposition/(correlative) conjunctions [17.1, 17.4]
4. A noun/noun/adjective [17.1, 17.3]
5. C interjection/adverb/adverb [17.3, 17.4]
6. A adjective/noun/adjective [17.1, 17.3]
7. A preposition/preposition/verb [17.2, 17.4]
8. E pronoun/pronoun/adjective [17.1, 17.3]
9. E pronoun/adverb/pronoun [17.1, 17.3]
10. C adverb/conjunction/adjective [17.3, 17.4]
11. A difficult and demanding [18.3]
12. C Do . . . know [18.2]
13. A owners [18.3]
14. C materials to choose and color schemes to select [18.2]
15. A Who [19.1]
16. C training a good staff [18.3]
17. C the very best [18.3]
18. E advantage [18.3]
19. A diners [19.1]
20. C you (understood) [18.2]
21. E infinitive phrase [19.2]
22. A appositive phrase [19.1]
23. E participial phrase [19.2]
24. C gerund phrase [19.2]

25. C participial phrase [19.2]
26. C nominative absolute [19.2]
27. C gerund phrase [19.2]
28. A participial phrase [19.2]
29. E infinitive phrase [19.2]
30. E prepositional phrase [19.1]
31. C complex/if you visit the seashore in our region/adverb clause [19.3, 19.4]
32. A compound [19.4]
33. A compound-complex/which weigh more than river otters/adjective clause/than river otters (are)/elliptical clause [19.3, 19.4]
34. E simple [19.4]
35. C complex/what constitutes the basic unit of sea otter society/noun clause [19.3, 19.4]
36. E *Sample:* Ramadan is the ninth month of the Islamic calendar. [20.2]
37. A *Sample:* Muslims adopt a special routine during Ramadan, which is designated as a month for fasting. [20.5]
38. E *Sample:* Every day the fast starts at dawn, and the precise moment is determined by the point at which one can distinguish a white thread from a black one. [20.2]
39. A *Sample:* The fast ends each day at sunset; then, prayers are said and passages from the Koran are recited. [20.4]
40. C *Sample:* According to the Koran, Muslims may neither eat nor drink during the fast. [20.2]
41. C *Sample:* Exempted from the fast are young children and very old people. [20.3]
42. E *Sample:* To determine the dates of holidays, Muslims use a lunar calendar. [20.5]
43. E *Sample:* Ending the month of Ramadan, a special holiday called the Fast-Breaking is observed. [20.3]
44. E *Sample:* Muslims recite prayers and feast on this day. [20.2]
45. E *Sample:* Have you ever seen pictures of the Blue Mosque in Istanbul, Turkey? [20.1]
46. A were [21.3]
47. E grew [21.1]
48. A were developed [21.4]
49. A did not protect [21.2]
50. E is [21.1]
51. A used [21.2]
52. C borne [21.1]
53. E seemed [21.2]
54. E became [21.1]
55. C be [21.3]
56. A We [22.1]
57. C our [22.1]
58. E you're [22.1]
59. A whose [22.1]
60. A them [22.1]
61. A he [22.1]
62. E their [22.1]
63. C Who [22.2]
64. C I [22.2]
65. C whom [22.2]
66. E is [23.1]
67. E is [23.1]
68. C is [23.1]

69. A eat [23.1]
70. C furnishes [23.1]
71. C are [23.1]
72. E are [23.1]
73. A his or her [23.2]
74. C is [23.2]
75. A its [23.2]
76. E are [23.2]
77. C his [23.2]
78. C its [23.2]
79. A has [23.2]
80. C have [23.1]
81. A anything else [24.2]
82. E more famous [24.1]
83. E worse [24.1]
84. A best [24.1]
85. C farther [24.2]
86. A finer [24.1]
87. A Bob's [24.2]
88. A faster [24.1]
89. C grandest [24.1]
90. C further [24.2]
91. A affect [25.2]
92. A among [25.2]
93. E Nowhere [25.2]
94. A lose [25.2]
95. C different from [25.2]
96. E their [25.2]
97. E ever [25.1]
98. A already [25.2]
99. E because [25.2]
100. C fewer [25.2]
101. E How much do you know about the city of Newport, Rhode Island? [26]
102. A Refugees from Massachusetts Bay Colony founded Newport in 1639. [26]
103. A Early in the American Revolution, British forces occupied the city. [26]
104. E Newport is the site or Trinity Church and Touro Synagogue. [26]
105. C In the nineteenth century, wealthy families like the Vanderbilts built mansions there. [26]
106. E Many of the mansions are now museums maintained by the Newport Historical Society. [26]
107. A The America's Cup—a sailing race—used to be held in the Atlantic Ocean off Newport. [26]
108. A Newport's Jacqueline Bouvier married Senator John F. Kennedy in September 1953. [26]
109. C When Kennedy served as President of the United States, Mrs. Kennedy was a popular First Lady. [26]
110. E She is noted for supervising the restoration of the White House. [26]
111. C Francisco Goya (1746–1828), one of Spain's greatest painters, was born in Fuendetodos. [27.2, 27.5]
112. A At the age of fourteen, Goya was apprenticed to José Luzan and spent four years in Luzan's studio. [27.2, 27.6]
113. E In 1763, however, Goya left for Madrid, Spain. [27.2]
114. A At the start of his career, Goya designed a series of tapestries noted for their grace, wit, and charm. [27.2]

115. C   Rejecting traditional themes, Goya depicted open-air amusements attended by the upper-class Spaniards. [27.2, 27.6]
116. E   Goya spent 1771 in Italy, and it is clear that he lived for some time in Rome. [27.2]
117. A   Goya returned to Spain around 1773; a dozen years later, he was appointed court painter. [27.2, 27.3]
118. A   Goya's portraits, which do not idealize their subjects, show him to be a keen observer. [27.2]
119. C   In 1793, a near-fatal illness left the artist totally deaf. [27.2, 27.6]
120. C   Goya, who favored social reform, often portrayed the nobility with a sharp, satirical eye. [27.2]
121. A   After Napoleon invaded Spain in 1808, Goya's paintings often protested war's savagery. [27.2, 27.6]
122. C   The bloodshed of May 3, 1808, is the subject of one of Goya's finest paintings. [27.2, 27.6]
123. C   Goya also completed a powerful series of etchings entitled The Disasters of War. [27.4]
124. A   Some of Goya's last works offer frightening, almost nightmarish images. [27.2, 27.6]
125. C   Goya lived in self-imposed exile in Bordeaux, France, in the last years of his life. [27.2, 27.6]

Chapter 17: The Parts of Speech (p. 158)
1. A   abstract, singular, compound, common
2. A   concrete, singular, compound, common
3. E   concrete, singular, proper
4. C   concrete, singular, common
5. C   abstract, singular, compound, common
6. A   concrete, singular, collective, common
7. E   concrete, plural, common
8. C   abstract, singular, proper
9. A   abstract, singular, common
10. A   concrete, plural, compound, common
11. A   Which, events, interrogative; that, events, relative; itself, war, intensive
12. C   all, those, indefinite; those, historians, demonstrative; whom, those, relative; you, personal
13. E   Everyone, (no antecedent), indefinite; they, Everyone, personal
14. A   itself, Europe, reflexive; no one, (no antecedent), indefinite
15. E   who, Americans, relative; that, war, relative; they, Americans, personal; theirs, Americans, personal; it, war, personal
16. E   attacked, AV, T
17. C   was, LV, I
18. A   described, AV, T
19. C   seemed, LV, I
20. C   Might have triumphed, AV, I
21. A   clearly, adverb, showed; modern, adjective, technology; forever, adverb, had changed
22. C   heavy, adjective, artillery; especially, adverb, decisive; decisive, adjective, invention

23. C   new, adjective, weaponry; trench adjective, warfare; inevitable, adjective, warfare; grisly, adjective, warfare
24. C   only, adverb, six; six, adjective, months; nearly, adverb, 500,000; German, adjective, soldiers; dead, adverb, lay
25. A   Almost, adverb, incredibly; incredibly, adverb, lasted; single, adjective, battle; five, adjective, months
26. A   both . . . and
27. C   like, for
28. A   Furthermore
29. E   Not only . . . but also, and
30. E   Wow!
31. A   verb
32. E   noun
33. E   noun
34. A   adjective
35. E   noun
36. A   verb
37. A   adjective
38. C   pronoun
39. C   adjective
40. A   verb
41. A   adverb
42. E   pronoun
43. C   pronoun
44. A   adjective
45. A   adverb
46. E   noun
47. A   preposition
48. E   conjunction
49. A   adjective
50. E   verb
51. A   B
52. A   J
53. A   C
54. E   F
55. A   D
56. A   H
57. A   B
58. E   J
59. A   B
60. A   F

Chapter 18: Basic Sentence Parts (p. 162)
1. A   Body temperature|declines dramatically during hibernation.
2. E   The ground squirrel|is a good example of a hibernator.
3. E   Squirrels|prepare for hibernation by doubling their body weight.
4. E   They|dig a deep burrow in the ground.
5. A   The squirrel|then curls itself up inside a small side pocket of the burrow.
6. A   The animal's heart rate|gradually slows down from 350 beats a minute to only 2–4 beats.
7. C   Body temperatures of hibernating squirrels|can drop by as much as 60 degrees Fahrenheit.
8. A   The squirrel's metabolic activity|plunges by 98 percent.
9. C   Its body temperature|inexplicably fluctuates and sometimes returns to normal.
10. A   Bears and bats|also hibernate.
11. A   marsupial; is

12. A you; <u>Can name</u>
13. C <u>opossum</u>; <u>is Taking</u>
14. E <u>opossum</u>; <u>is</u>
15. C <u>infant</u>; <u>lives</u>
16. C (you); <u>tell</u>
17. C <u>those</u>; <u>Do include</u>
18. A <u>photos, drawings</u>; <u>are</u>
19. E (you); <u>Look</u>
20. A <u>animals</u>; <u>live</u>
21. A animals (predicate nominative)
22. E nocturnal (predicate adjective)
23. A themselves (direct object)
24. C animals (direct object); study (objective complement)
25. A home (direct object)
26. C ratels (direct objects); courageous (objective complement)
27. C second (predicate adjective)
28. E honey, larvae (direct objects)
29. C ratel (indirect object); location (direct object)
30. A species (direct object)
31. E simple predicate
32. A simple subject
33. A predicate nominative
34. E direct object
35. E direct object
36. C simple subject
37. C indirect object
38. E simple subject
39. C objective complement
40. A predicate adjective
41. A C
42. A A
43. A D
44. C C
45. C A

Chapter 19: Phrases and Clauses (p. 165)
1. A appositive phrase, Nat "King" Cole
2. A adjective phrase, daughter
3. A adverb phrase, chose
4. A adverb phrase, studied
5. E appositive phrase, *Inseparable*
6. A appositive phrase, honors
7. A adjective phrase, star
8. C appositive phrase, album
9. E adjective phrase, duet
10. C adverb phrase, accompanied
11. A participial phrase
12. A gerund
13. E infinitive phrase
14. A gerund phrase
15. C nominative absolute
16. E infinitive
17. E participle
18. E participle
19. A participal phrase
20. C gerund phrase
21. A who Barbra Streisand is (noun)
22. E who was born in Brooklyn (adjective)
23. A as her acting (is) (elliptical)
24. E When Streisand was twenty-two (adverb)
25. C that she charmed audiences with her intuitive talent (noun)
26. E After *Funny Girl* took Broadway by storm (adverb)
27. A that were huge hits (adjective)

28. A than acting (is) (elliptical)
29. E which is based on a story by Isaac Bashevis Singer (adjective)
30. C that Streisand was an extremely talented director (noun)
31. E complex
32. A simple
33. C compound-complex
34. A complex
35. A compound
36. A C
37. C F
38. A D
39. C H
40. A B

Chapter 20: Effective Sentences (p. 169)
1. E declarative /.
2. E interrogative /?
3. A imperative /.
4. E declarative /.
5. E exclamatory /!
6. E *Sample:* Elias Howe and Isaac Singer helped create the sewing machine.
7. A *Sample:* Elias Howe, a Boston merchant, hoped to develop a machine to duplicate his wife's hand-stitching motions.
8. A *Sample:* When that effort failed, Howe devised a new kind of stitch.
9. A *Sample:* Howe's machine, which could produce 250 stitches a minute, impressed manufacturers.
10. C *Sample:* Produced three years later, Isaac Singer's machine was more versatile and sold for one third the price.
11. E *Sample:* For centuries, judges in China wore tinted glasses.
12. E *Sample:* Surprisingly, these early glasses did not aim to reduce glare.
13. A *Sample:* Hiding their eyes, the judges sought to conceal their reactions during a court case.
14. C *Sample:* In the twentieth century came true sunglasses.
15. A *Sample:* To reduce glare at high altitudes, early pilots wore these sunglasses.
16. E *Sample:* Jonas Hanway was a successful businessman who lived in eighteenth-century England.
17. E *Sample:* Hanway made a fortune by trading with Russia and the Far East.
18. A correct
19. A *Sample:* On the streets of London, Hanway always carried an umbrella. It made no difference whether the weather was rainy or fair.
20. C *Sample:* Because of the frequent showers in their city, Londoners gradually realized that an umbrella was a wise investment.
21. A *Sample:* The metal can has been in existence since only 1810.
22. C *Sample:* Britain's navy found cans convenient as a means of supplying rations to sailors.
23. E *Sample:* Before 1820, cans were brought to America as containers for food preservation.

248 • Answers

© Prentice-Hall, Inc.

24. A *Sample:* Although cans were virtually ignored for forty years, the Civil War popularized them.

25. E *Sample:* Soldiers on both sides needed preserved military rations.

26. E *Sample:* However, for half a century early cans were not easy to open.

27. C *Sample:* Soldiers use hammers and bayonets to open cans, which were thick-walled and weighed as much as a pound.

28. A *Sample:* Hoping to improve the situation, Ezra J. Warner invented the first patented can opener.

29. C *Sample:* To access the can's contents, a person had to move the opener's blade carefully around the rim.

30. A *Sample:* Although Warner's can opener was unpopular with the public, the military used it.

31. E *Sample:* Chess, checkers, and backgammon have been popular since ancient times.

32. A *Sample:* In ancient Egypt, a game called senet was played by peasants, artisans, and rulers.

33. E *Sample:* Each senet player moved ivory or stone pieces across a papyrus playing board.

34. A *Sample:* Historians argue over whether chess was invented in India or Persia.

35. E *Sample:* Thousands of years ago, people enjoyed playing games, running races, and wrestling.

36. A *Sample:* For centuries people had only simple means of washing their clothes. On sea voyages, they would put their laundry in a bag and let the ship drag it in the water.

37. A *Sample:* The first hand-operated washing machines used a device called a "dolly," which fitted into a tub and pummeled the clothes.

38. C *Sample:* Many odd inventions to wash clothes were devised, but it is generally agreed that actual washing machines first appeared in the early 1800's.

39. C *Sample:* The earliest washing machines were wooden boxes; the user tumbled the box by using a hand crank.

40. A *Sample:* Taking turns, mothers and daughters cranked the box's handle.

41. A B
42. A D
43. E A
44. A C
45. A A

Chapter 21: Verb Usage (p. 173)

1. C present perfect, progressive
2. E past, emphatic
3. A future perfect, basic
4. E present, basic
5. A past perfect, basic
6. A it had grown
7. E I do prepare
8. A they will have sold
9. C we were digging
10. A you did draw
11. A strove

12. E grew
13. E arose
14. A struck
15. E blown
16. C lay
17. C shrunk
18. A frozen
19. A brought
20. E fought
21. E had
22. E kept
23. C had become
24. A saw
25. E was
26. C had begun
27. E produced
28. E appeared
29. E enjoy
30. A will receive
31. E were
32. A correct
33. C study
34. A be
35. C check
36. A are started, passive
37. E aids, active
38. A will reach, active
39. A might have been improved, passive
40. C have been admired, passive
41. A D
42. E J
43. C B
44. A H
45. C D

Chapter 22: Pronoun Usage (p. 175)

1. E their, possessive
2. A her; objective
3. E my; possessive
4. E we; nominative
5. E its; possessive
6. A us; objective
7. C you; objective
8. A she; nominative
9. E me; objective
10. E I; nominative
11. A us; indirect object
12. E I; subject
13. A its; ownership
14. A We; subject
15. C she; predicate nominative
16. A them; object of a preposition
17. C their; ownership
18. E us; object of a verbal
19. E Their; ownership
20. C we; predicate nominative
21. E *Sample:* I; subject
22. A *Sample:* We; subject
23. A *Sample:* I; predicate nominative
24. A *Sample:* she; predicate nominative
25. C *Sample:* We; nominative absolute
26. A *Sample:* me; object of a preposition
27. C *Sample:* her; subject of an infinitive
28. A *Sample:* us; object of a participle
29. E *Sample:* her; direct object
30. C *Sample:* us; indirect object
31. C Who; subject
32. A Whom; direct object

33. A who; subject
34. A whom; object of a preposition
35. E Whose; ownership
36. A I
37. C them
38. A me
39. A I
40. A we
41. A C
42. C F
43. A A
44. E G
45. A D

Chapter 23: Agreement (p. 177)
1. E are
2. A are
3. C makes
4. E feature
5. A are
6. A is
7. A have
8. A seems
9. C is
10. A do
11. E tries
12. C are
13. A listens
14. A brings
15. A are
16. A his
17. A his or her
18. E themselves
19. C them
20. E their
21. E his
22. A his
23. A he
24. E their
25. A it
26. A it
27. A his
28. E they
29. A his or her
30. C their
31. A *Sample:* Tall tales are humorous, exaggerated stories that people tell as if they were fact.
32. E *Sample:* When Maria told Denise some tall tales about Pecos Bill, Denise could not stop laughing.
33. A *Sample:* In the Old West, passengers on stagecoach rides swapped tall tales. Storytelling made the time go by faster.
34. A *Sample:* Both Mike Fink and Davy Crockett were real frontiersmen whose adventures were exaggerated in the retelling. The stories were very popular.
35. C *Sample:* In the 1800s, Crockett was such a popular figure that people heard his story everywhere.
36. A *Sample:* Crockett was an adventurer, cowboy, war hero, and Congressman. Even without exaggeration, his life was pretty amazing.

37. C *Sample:* Like Davy Crockett, Daniel Boone was a real-life frontiersman whose life became legendary. The fact that these men were real makes the stories more interesting.
38. E *Sample:* Paul Bunyan and Pecos Bill lived only in folk tales. They both had outrageous exploits. Folk tales are popular in many countries.
39. C *Sample:* Paul Bunyan and his blue ox, Babe, roamed the northern forests. The forests were the perfect setting for stories about a giant lumberjack.
40. A *Sample:* New tall tales continue to appear; one often hears them in the routines of stand-up comics.
41. E C
42. A B
43. C D
44. A C
45. C E

Chapter 24: Using Modifiers (p. 180)
1. E prettier, prettiest
2. E more sympathetic, most sympathetic
3. A more wisely, most wisely
4. C worse, worst
5. E more majestic, most majestic
6. C worse, worst
7. C lovelier, loveliest
8. E more gracefully, most gracefully
9. E faster, fastest
10. C more rapid, most rapid
11. A farther, farthest; or further, furthest
12. C better, best
13. C costlier, costliest
14. A more foolish, most foolish
15. E odder, oddest
16. E comparative
17. C positive
18. A superlative
19. C comparative
20. E superlative
21. E smaller
22. C more
23. A tinier
24. A further
25. C less
26. E earlier
27. A latest
28. E best
29. A more
30. C costlier
31. E The art of watchmaking is unique.
32. A For generations of watchmakers, overcoming friction was more important than anything else.
33. A Are Swiss watches made better than any other watch?
34. E *Sample:* Watchmaking in Japan is almost as good as it is in Switzerland.
35. A My Japanese watch is better than any other watch I've ever owned.
36. A *Sample:* No two watches are more similar than the two Jan owns.
37. C *Sample:* Is the accuracy of a clock better than that of a watch?
38. A I like an older clock with a pendulum better than any other kind of clock.

39. C *Sample:* In winter a clock's pendulum swings faster than it does in summer.
40. C Do atomic clocks keep better time than other clocks do?
41. A D
42. C H
43. E A
44. A J
45. C C
46. A F
47. A C
48. A H
49. E C
50. A F

Chapter 25: Miscellaneous Problems in Usage (p. 183)

1. E *Sample:* Before last summer, we hadn't ever been to Washington, D.C.
2. A *Sample:* There probably isn't any other city more interesting to visit.
3. E *Sample:* You have no idea how impressive the monuments are!
4. A *Sample:* We barely had time to see all the tourist attractions.
5. C *Sample:* We had but a long weekend to spend in Washington.
6. C *Sample:* We could spend scarcely an hour at the Lincoln Memorial.
7. A *Sample:* There was no one who wanted to miss the White House.
8. A *Sample:* Hardly any of the sites we visited charged admission.
9. E *Sample:* Didn't anybody use a camera during the trip?
10. C correct
11. E *Sample:* A visit to the Washington Monument is not uninteresting.
12. A *Sample:* The sight of the Capitol dome is not uninspiring.
13. E *Sample:* Most visitors to Washington are not unhappy with their experience.
14. E *Sample:* Visitors find that the city is not unexciting.
15. A *Sample:* The floodlighting of many public buildings at night is not unattractive.
16. E a while
17. A proceeded
18. E Because
19. E outside
20. A may
21. C a
22. A lose
23. A than
24. E Every one
25. C each other's
26. C fewer
27. A into
28. C Besides
29. A eager
30. E gone
31. A *Sample:* The Statue of Liberty is one of New York's principal tourist attractions.
32. C *Sample:* One reason the statue is popular is that it is a symbol of freedom.
33. E *Sample:* Before our visit there, I never knew anything about the monument.
34. E *Sample:* From history books, I should have known it was a gift from France.

35. C *Sample:* The organization that gave us the statue was the Franco-American Union.
36. A *Sample:* Liberty Island, where the statue stands, lies in Upper New York Bay.
37. C *Sample:* Visitors making their way to the crown must climb no fewer than 354 steps.
38. A Correct
39. E *Sample:* Hardly any immigrant entry point used to be busier than Ellis Island.
40. A *Sample:* We toured the Ellis Island museum all together but split up outside.
41. A A
42. E B
43. A A
44. C B
45. C D

Chapter 26: Capitalization (p. 186)

1. A Oh, Marvelous, We
2. A Where
3. E My, We
4. A He
5. C Something
6. E Hungarian, proper adjective
7. A Missouri, proper noun
8. A July, proper adjective
9. A Swedish-speaking, proper adjective
10. E Senator Barbara Boxer, proper noun
11. A Easter, proper adjective
12. A Laurel O'Boyle, M.D., proper noun
13. E *Lad, a Dog,* proper noun
14. C American, proper adjective
15. C Elm, proper adjective; Oak, proper adjective
16. A Straddling, North Carolina-Tennessee, Great Smoky Mountains National Park, Congress
17. E With, United States
18. A The, Appalachian Trail, Mt. Katahdin, Maine, Springer Mountain, Georgia.
19. E Last, Governor Ann E. Brady, Sierra Club
20. E Within, Europe
21. A Yosemite National Park, West
22. C It, Sierra Nevada, California
23. A My, Carla, Peruvian, Carla
24. C They, Thursday, Thanksgiving Day, West Coast, November
25. C Carla, Girl Scouts, Zipomatic, Swiss Army
26. E 2620 North Magnolia Street
   Chicago, Illinois 60614
27. E June 1, 20--
28. A Mrs. Thelma Ryan
   2314 Carol View Drive
   Cardiff, California 92007
29. C My dear Aunt Thelma,
30. A Very truly yours,
31. E For American citizens, elections are held the first Tuesday after the first Monday in November.
32. E Every four years, the President of the United States is inaugurated on January 20 at noon.
33. C Before the Twentieth Amendment to the Constitution was ratified in 1933, however, the President was inaugurated in early March.

34. C   My uncle, Louis D. Pezza, Jr., always celebrates the Fourth of July with a cookout at his home on Park and Main streets.

35. E   Memorial Day, formerly called Decoration Day, was first observed in 1868 to honor the Civil War dead.

36. A   Did you know that Labor Day, which falls on the first Monday in September, is celebrated in both the U.S. and Canada?

37. A   In late November, Thanksgiving Day recalls the harvest of the Pilgrim settlers at Plymouth Colony in 1621.

38. A   The New York Symphony Orchestra will celebrate New Year's Day with a special concert at Lincoln Center.

39. C   Will ex-Senator Gordon be appointed president of Duke University, one of the finest universities in the South?

40. A   I asked Grandmother and Aunt Nelly if they would come east to visit us around Mother's Day.

41. C   B
42. E   C
43. A   D
44. A   A
45. C   C

Chapter 27: Punctuation (p. 189)

1. E   world.
2. E   Africa?
3. C   Wow!, magnificent!
4. A   Dr., capital.
5. A   P.M.
6. E   Channel,
7. A   agricultural, and, rice, coffee, vanilla, and
8. A   resources, minerals,
9. C   historians, 2,000
10. A   1500,
11. A   forested;
12. A   treasure:
13. C   "endemic":
14. A   following:
15. C   arboreal;
16. E   "If you are interested in lemurs," said Mr. Sanders, "you may want to consult some reference books in the library."
17. A   "An excellent book on the island's fauna is Mammals of Madagascar by Nick Garbutt," he continued.
18. A   Mr. Sanders told us that the author included a useful chapter called "Conservation and Protected Areas."
19. E   Recently, I read a magazine article in Time entitled "A Global Green Deal."
20. C   Is that the article in which the author says, "We have in hand most of the technologies needed to chart a new course"?
21. A   So far, scientists have identified numerous species—1.75 million—but this may be only the beginning.
22. C   The total number of species (as we learned at the Museum of Natural History) may be as great as 100 million.
23. A   Tropical rain forests—you may be amazed to discover—are thought to contain more than half the species on earth.

24. A   According to an article I read recently, "It [biodiversity] is a complex web of plant and animal species."
25. E   Gifford Pinchot (1865–1946) was one of President Theodore Roosevelt's strongest allies in support for conservation.
26. E   correct
27. A   correct
28. E   up-to-date statistics
29. A   third-largest island
30. C   self-possessed ex-governor
31. A   sociable mothers-in-law
32. A   mid-March madness
33. C   ten-minute free-for-all
34. A   five-year-old child
35. A   German-born biologist
36. A   the rain forest's medicinal plants
37. E   couldn't
38. E   they're
39. C   India and Nepal's borders
40. A   its sound
41. E   C
42. C   J
43. E   A
44. A   G
45. A   C

Grammar, Usage, and Mechanics: Cumulative Mastery Test (p. 192)

The numbers in brackets indicate the chapter and section of the skills being tested.

1. E   preposition/noun/verb [17.1, 17.2, 17.4]
2. C   adverb/adverb [17.2]
3. A   conjunction/noun [17.1, 17.4]
4. E   adjective/noun/adverb [17.1, 17.3]
5. A   adjective/preposition [17.3, 17.4]
6. C   noun/adjective/adverb [17.1, 17.3]
7. C   adjective/adverb/adjective [17.3]
8. A   adjective/pronoun [17.3, 17.4]
9. A   verb/noun/noun [17.1, 17.2]
10. C   interjection/adverb/adjective [17.3, 17.4]
11. A   tricky/fulfilling [18.3]
12. C   schemes/fabrics [18.2]
13. A   Who [18.1]
14. A   Ann [18.3]
15. A   best [18.3]
16. E   challenge [18.3]
17. E   invented [18.1]
18. E   invention [18.3]
19. A   fashionable [18.3]
20. C   samples [18.2]
21. A   participial phrase [19.2]
22. A   infinitive phrase [19.2]
23. A   gerund phrase [19.2]
24. E   prepositional phrase [19.1]
25. E   participial phrase [19.2]
26. C   nominative absolute [19.2]
27. E   appositive phrase [19.1]
28. A   infinitive phrase [19.2]
29. E   prepositional phrase [19.1]
30. A   gerund phrase [19.2]
31. A   complex/which include frogs, toads, and salamanders/ (adjective) [19.3, 19.4]
32. E   compound [19.4]
33. C   complex/that the eggs of amphibians are softer than reptiles' eggs/ (noun); than reptiles' eggs/ (elliptical) [19.3, 19.4]

34. A compound-complex/when they reach adulthood/(adverb) [19.3, 19.4]
35. A simple [19.4]
36. E *Sample:* Sociologists have carried out studies indicating that pets are good for the elderly. [20.4]
37. C *Sample:* If you are suffering from stress, you will often benefit by getting a pet. [20.5]
38. A *Sample:* Most people need companionship, and single elderly people often suffer from loneliness. [20.2]
39. A *Sample:* Some elderly people have only a few friends left in the neighborhood; others have trouble making new friends. [20.4]
40. E *Sample:* For all these reasons, health experts have recommended that older people keep a pet. [20.3]
41. A *Sample:* To care for a dog or a cat properly, the owner must sometimes make special provisions. [20.5]
42. E *Sample:* An affectionate pet offers love and companionship. [20.2]
43. C *Sample:* Especially popular with older people are cats. [20.3]
44. A *Sample:* Experts increasingly recognize the positive effect of pets on older people. [20.5]
45. E *Sample:* Have you seen a photograph of Mrs. Delaney's cats and Mr. Delgado's dogs? [20.6]
46. C were [21.3]
47. A seem [21.1]
48. A would be [21.2]
49. E form [21.2]
50. C lain [21.1]
51. E grown [21.1]
52. A appears [21.2]
53. C led [21.1]
54. E is [21.2]
55. A will defeat [21.2]
56. A We [22.1]
57. E she [22.1]
58. E her [22.1]
59. A Who [22.2]
60. A whom [22.2]
61. C whoever [22.2]
62. C he [22.1]
63. A us [22.1]
64. C I [22.2]
65. E hers [22.1]
66. E are [23.1]
67. A is [23.1]
68. C is [23.1]
69. A is [23.1]
70. A works [23.1]
71. C have [23.1]
72. A its [23.2]
73. A is [23.1]
74. A was [23.1]
75. C illustrates [23.1]
76. A his or her [23.2]
77. E I [23.2]
78. A are [23.1]
79. C one [23.2]
80. A is [23.1]
81. A best [24.1]

82. A any other [24.2]
83. E cutest [24.1]
84. C Farther [25.2]
85. A Donna's [24.2]
86. E closer [24.1]
87. A more complex [24.1]
88. C unique [24.2]
89. A worst [24.1]
90. A anyone else [24.2]
91. E ever [25.1]
92. E anywhere [25.2]
93. E ever [25.1]
94. A Except [25.2]
95. C lay [25.2]
96. C farthest [25.2]
97. C one another [25.2]
98. E Every one [25.2]
99. A already [25.2]
100. A among [25.2]
101. E The, Italian, Pisa [26]
102. A Haven't, Cousin Norm's, Leaning Tower of Pisa [26]
103. E Norm, Skip and Paul, Italy, August [26]
104. A In, European, Eiffel Tower, Paris, France [26]
105. A This, French, Alexandre Gustave Eiffel, Paris Exposition [26]
106. C My, Alice, Mom [26]
107. E About, Eiffel Tower, New York City, Brooklyn Bridge [26]
108. A Here, I, This, East River, Brooklyn, Manhattan [26]
109. C Does, Brooklyn, Flatbush, Fulton [26]
110. C Rona, Dr. Petry, Is, Sharpe's, Prospect Park, Brooklyn [26]
111. C Winslow Homer (1836–1910), who is often said to rank among America's finest painters, was born in Boston, Massachusetts. [27.2, 27.5]
112. A Homer showed artistic talent as a child, but nineteenth-century Boston offered its residents few opportunities for training in art. [27.2, 27.6]
113. E In a dissatisfying period of apprenticeship, Homer worked for a two-year stint with a Boston lithographer. [27.2, 27.6]
114. A Didn't he then decide to move to New York City, where he hoped to make a career as an illustrator? [27.1, 27.2, 27.6]
115. E Homer attended night classes in drawing, illustrating, and oil painting. [27.2]
116. C Then he won an assignment from the magazine Harper's Weekly to cover the Civil War as an artist-illustrator. [27.4, 27.6]
117. A Homer's war sketches, which he later converted into engravings and oil paintings, often focused on the soldiers' daily routine in camp. [27.2, 27.6]
118. C The artist's notable Civil War paintings include the following: The Brierwood Pipe (1864), The Bright Side (1865), and A Rainy Day in Camp (1871). [27.2, 27.4, 27.5]
119. A Here is a reproduction of another of Homer's masterpieces, The Veteran in a New Field. [27.2, 27.4]

120. A   In France, after the war, Homer was influenced by the Barbizon School, a group of pre-Impressionist French painters who did landscapes in a realistic style. [27.2, 27.6]

121. C   As this pamphlet "Homer's Art" explains, Homer abandoned illustration in 1876 and devoted the rest of his career to oil painting and watercolors. [27.2, 27.4]

122. A   Among his best-known works—you have probably seen some of them before—are his paintings of the sea. [27.5]

123. C   "Some of Homer's watercolors," said our art teacher, Mr. Gonzaga, "are as good as his best oil paintings." [27.2, 27.4]

124. A   Mark asked, "What is your favorite seascape by Homer, Alice?" [27.1, 27.2, 27.4]

125. A   "If I had to make a choice," Alice replied, "it would be The Fog Warning." [27.4]

Chapter 28: Speaking, Listening, Viewing, and Representing (p. 201)

1. E   a. *Sample:* All of the other answers would not be helpful in a discussion.

2. E   *Sample:* What kinds of new activities could we offer?
The answer is relevant, because it addresses the problem.

3. A   a. *Sample:* This is the only answer that is constructive and that offers an example.

4. A   c, d, a, b

5. A   informative, *Sample:* because it involves presenting facts

6. A   extemporaneous, *Sample:* because it would be unplanned

7. A   *Sample:* Students could interview other students and store owners, both of whom would have direct knowledge of the problem

8. C   *Sample:* Problem: distrust and disrespect between owners and students; Students' Viewpoint: Students feel undervalued; Store owners' viewpoint; owners feel that they are losing customers; Reason for Trying to Solve Problem: to encourage better community relations; Possible Solution: Students and store owners agree to sit down and talk and agree on a compromise.

9. E   c. *Sample:* Hand gestures are a nonverbal strategy for providing emphasis.

10. A   *Samples:* a. The speaker supported his ideas with appropriate details, so I understood every point he made.
b. Occasionally, he didn't speak loudly enough.

11. E   *Sample:* A speaker needs to show his interest in the audience.

12. A   *Samples:* You can test your understanding by rephrasing the speaker's ideas in your own words. You can talk to another person and compare what you both got out of it.

13. A   c, b, a, d

14. A   c, a, b, d

15. C   *Samples:* a. When did this problem come to your attention? b. How many cars are speeding during the lunch hour? c. Why should we do something about it? d. Do you think the problem will get better on its own?

16. A   a. *Sample:* You can only check accuracy with someone else, if you are unsure of your work.

17. A   b. *Sample:* The other information is not historical.

18. A   *Sample:* that England and France were both dominant presences in the Middle East

19. C   *Sample:* Jewish settlements were near the water, which helped them to irrigate or transport materials.

20. A   d. *Sample:* This is the only answer that illustrates information that changes over time.

21. A   d. *Sample:* This is the only answer that supports the comparison of numbers or amounts.

22. A   *Sample:* to determine where the company is most successfully marketing its products.

23. A   b, c, d, a

24. A   b, c, d, a

25. E   c. *Sample:* Where the artist buys materials is irrelevant to art interpretation.

26. A   Students' explanations for their answers will vary. *Sample:* An illustration, such as a wartime photograph, would be very effective in conveying this devastation.

27. A   *Samples:* a. on the top, to get people's attention; b. use color, graphics, or photographs

28. A   *Sample:* I would use a model to show the structure of the theater, and slides of drawings showing how it was built.

29. A   d. *Sample:* This answer refers to scenery.

30. A   *Sample:* The mood would be poignant. I would use dimmed lighting, along with music that at first is light and hopeful and then becomes heavy and melancholy.

Chapter 29: Vocabulary and Spelling (p. 207)

1. E   d. *Sample:* Magazine articles may include new words.

2. C   *Samples:* a. inevitable (have to adjust to); b. present-day (world around us); c. factor (affects the college a student can get into); d. try (best efforts); e. goals (work hard to reach them)

3. E   full of sunshine (meaning happy, or glowing with happiness)

4. E   rock the boat (meaning to upset people)

5. A   c. *Sample:* uses the word in its technical, not figurative, context.

6. C   *Samples:* a. basic life (signs); b. significant; important

7. A   a. Students' examples will vary. *Sample:* The millionaire was *benevolent* and regularly donated money to charities.

8. A   d. Students' examples will vary. *Sample:* The mountain climber finally reached the *zenith* of the peak.

9. C 1. kitten, baby to adult; 2. song, artist to work; 3. sky, organism to environment; 4. calm, antonyms
10. A d. Both pairs of words are synonyms.
11. A *Sample:* A notebook can help you keep track of unfamiliar words you need to learn.
12. E *Samples:* a. Word origins can help readers deepen their understanding of the meaning of a word. b. Synonyms help writers to avoid repeating a word.
13. A *Sample:* He had to *haul* ten pounds of coal from the dock to the truck.
14. A a.
15. A c.
16. A a., because it is a geographical term
17. A *Sample: Portable* means "capable of being carried"; *transport* means "to carry."
18. A -sens-, to feel; -mono-, single or alone; -chron-, time
19. C sub-, below or under; mis-, wrong; un-, not
20. A -ful, full of; -less, without; -able, capable of
21. C *Samples:* greenhouse: a mainly glass building, in which the temperature can be regulated for the growing of plants; sandpaper: abrasive paper used for smoothing and polishing; tailgate: to drive too closely behind another vehicle; overcome: to master or prevail over
22. A *Sample:* Use the traditional rule *i* before *e* except after *c* or when sounded like *a*, as in *neighbor* or *weigh.*
23. A a.
       c.
       d.
       b.
24. A portraying; merriment; enjoyment; appliance
25. E disappear; misinform; unexpected; inappropriate
26. A mysteries; parties; alleys; tragedies, turkeys
27. C mothers-in-law; Canadian geese, all-stars, country mice
28. A night; rain; weather; whether
29. A *Sample:* English often borrows words from other languages and cultures. If students know the foreign language meaning of a word, it helps them remember the English meaning.
30. C democracy; exercise; privileges; courageous; opinion; received

Chapter 30: Reading Skills (p. 212)
1. E e, c, b, a, f, d
2. E *Sample:* to offer an idea of what the material is about, to break up text, and to divide material into sections and make it more digestible
3. E *Sample:* Previewing the chapter's questions and exercises gives you an idea of the focus of each chapter and the main points to look for as you read.
4. E *Sample:* It explains the picture.
5. A *Sample:* After the fall of France, Britain was getting ready to fight Germany.

6. A *Sample:* Churchill was a major force in getting Britain ready to fight; he was a forceful, persuasive speaker.
7. A *Sample:* Churchill had, for a long time, spoken out against the Nazis. He spoke powerfully, using phrases such as "We shall never surrender."
8. A *Sample:* It would depend on the purpose. If, for instance, I just wanted a general idea, I would skim the passage. If I needed to locate a particular piece of information, I would scan.
9. E d, c, b, a
10. A *Sample:* What is the English Bill of Rights?
11. A *Sample:* It is a document giving more power to Parliament.
12. A *Sample:* 1. Parliament offered the crown to William and Mary; 2. Parliament insisted they agree to the Bill of Rights.
13. A *Sample:* Main idea: growth of Parliament; Major detail #1: Parliament was an important body; Supporting details: It unified England; It came to acquire a larger role in government; Major detail #2: Parliament grew more powerful; Supporting details: It approved money for wars; it grew in size, with commoners added.
14. A *Sample:* A timeline would show changes in the monarchy over the years.
15. A *Sample:* Similarities: (overlapping section of Venn diagram circles): both musically talented and smart. Differences: (one of the non-overlapping sections): one is unique in that he plays flute and is short; (the other non-overlapping section): the other is unique in that she plays cello and is tall.
16. C *Sample:* Parliament gained power, and the monarchy lost power.
17. A *Sample:* It won the right to approve new taxes.
18. A *Sample:* A monarch might say that the king or queen should control the nation's money.
19. A Opinion; Fact; Fact; Opinion
20. A *Sample:* Therefore, it was clear that algae or other organisms could grow in the pond.
21. C *Sample:* Major premise: Citrus fruits contain Vitamin C. Minor premise: Oranges, grapefruits, lemons, and limes are citrus fruits.
Conclusion: Therefore, they contain Vitamin C.
22. A a. good logic; b. fallacy; c. fallacy; d. good logic
23. A a. unrelated; b. cause-and-effect; c. unrelated; d. cause-and-effect
24. C *Sample:* I optimistically planted a good variety of tulips in the fall, and this spring they are taking off like magic.
25. A *Sample:* The new ice cream shop has the traditional flavors, as well as some new ones.

26. C *Sample:* The department manager has decided to change the floor plan to enlarge the cubicles.
27. A *Sample:* Laura's canary died.
28. C *Sample:* Lots of effort has gone into this report.
29. C *Samples:* a. to question the validity of nonviolence in certain cases; b. Yes, his words are persuasive, since he mentions the cost of nonviolence.
30. A *Samples:* a. to feel like you are in the story; b. In *To Kill a Mockingbird*, I identified with the children and their father in their quest for humanity.
31. A *Sample:* Outside references broaden the reader's understanding of the writer's purpose.
32. A *Samples:* a. Drama is meant to be performed. b. The reader can act out the parts or read them aloud.
33. A *Sample:* Readers can appreciate the sounds and rhythms of poetry if they read it aloud. Images that appeal to the senses help you enjoy the poem.
34. A *Sample:* They can lend a personal perspective to a historical or cultural event.
35. A a. Newspapers typically provide information on current events.

Chapter 31: Study, Reference, and Test-Taking Skills (p. 218)
1. E *Sample:* keeping an organized study notebook. This allows students to keep track of assignments and their due dates.
2. E *Sample:* Keep study area quiet and well-lit, allow enough time for studying each day, keep a notebook with each day's assignments.
3. E *Sample:* I could have allowed more time each day for studying.
4. A *Sample:* Main idea: The Hundred Years' War was between England and France. Details: It occurred between 1337 and 1453; England wanted to hold onto lands it had owned in France; Edward III claimed French crown in 1337.
5. A *Sample:* The Hundred Years' War came to pass due to several factors, all based on different concepts about the land that England and France should possess. It was fueled by economic rivalry and national pride.
6. A *Sample:* England and France fought a number of battles between 1337 and 1453, known as the Hundred Years' war.
7. A *Samples:* a. author and title information; b. In case you don't know all of the information, you can locate a book using the information you do have.
8. A a. The availability of a book is immediately apparent on an electronic catalog.
9. A a. nonfiction
    b. *Sample:* to make it easier to locate books on related subjects
10. A *Di-. Sample:* Novels are shelved by author's last name, alphabetically.

11. C *Di-. Sample:* Biographies are shelved by subject, alphabetically.
12. A b. *Sample:* This is the most specific and topic-relevant subject choice.
13. E d.
14. A *Samples:* encyclopedias, periodicals
15. C *Sample:* periodicals, since they would have the most updated information
16. A *Sample:* a. You might locate a primary source, such as an original letter.
    b. It tells you how current the information is.
17. C *Sample:* You might wish to include some information in your paper about famous stuntmen who did skydiving stunts.
18. A a. specialized
    b. abridged
    c. unabridged
19. E void—vortex: volume; volume—voted: voluminous; vocabulary—voice: vocal; virtue—vital: vision
20. C *Sample:* It is useful to a speaker, so that he or she can feel comfortable using the word in conversation.
21. E the first syllable
22. E *Samples:* 1. There was a *volley* of fire from the cannons. 2. We played doubles, and my partner hit a really good *volley* at the net.
23. A *Sample:* The original words mean "flight" and "to fly," which directly relate to the current definition of something that is in flight.
24. A a. almanac
    b. atlas
    c. thesaurus
    d. encyclopedia
25. C *Sample:* They can provide richer insights and experiences that affect students in several ways at once (auditory, visual, emotional).
26. A *Sample:* I would check the sponsor of the site or the credentials of the source or look at the address to see whether it has "org," "edu," or some other reliable location in the address.
27. A d. *Sample:* None of the other answers have to do with previewing a test.
28. C *Samples:* You should skip questions you can't answer so that you don't run out of time to complete the test. Also, in standardized tests, you are sometimes penalized more for guessing incorrectly than for omitting an answer.
29. A 1. c
    2. a
    3. d
    4. b
30. A c. *Sample:* "the British constitution is made up of all acts of Parliament . . . as well as unwritten traditions"
31. C a. False
    b. True
    c. True
    d. False
32. C *Sample:* law
33. A d. *Sample:* legal/illegal

34. C   a. enthusiasm : sports fan; *Sample:* quality to individual person

35. E   d. *Sample:* This is the only answer that deals with test preparation.

Chapter 32: Workplace Skills and Competencies (p. 224)

1. E   *Samples:* Rehearse an intimidating situation, such as an interview, with your friends or parents. Practice interviewing skills, such as listening closely and choosing words carefully.

2. E   *Sample:* 1 I would call to get the name of the interviewer and some background on their experience; 2 I could read the camp's brochure.

3. A   d. This is the only answer that deals with the interview itself.

4. A   *Sample:* Write a thank-you letter that expresses strong interest in the job.

5. A   *Sample:* Knowing when to be serious or funny shows that you are aware of the group's mood and helps the group interact effectively.

6. A   *Sample:* You can express your admiration for the things she does well before you list any problems.

7. A   *Sample:* You do not want to create an atmosphere of blame. It is better to state your concern that you may not finish on time and ask for ideas about how you can work together to achieve your mutual goal.

8. A   *Sample:* They can listen to one another's ideas without being critical.

9. A   *Sample:* The facilitator leads the discussion and gives everyone a chance to speak.

10. C   *Sample:* Accept criticism; take nothing personally. Additionally, if the criticism seems unwarranted or overly personal, they may address it after the meeting, privately.

11. A   *Sample:* It keeps the meeting on track so it doesn't run too long.

12. A   *Sample:* a. He or she might try small steps, such as taking an escalator. b. He or she might take a class at night to learn about the baking business.

13. A   *Sample:* I could look up internships on-line or look in the Yellow Pages to find someone local to talk to.

14. A   *Sample:* Problem—not enough parking; Solution #1—Ask businesses to let students park; Solution #2—Ask residents to let students park on street; People to Involve—Students, teachers, administrators, neighbors, local business owners, school board members

15. C   *Sample:* 1. Problem—We need to increase parking spaces; 2. Solution #1—Could we pay anybody for spaces? Solution #2—Can we get a law passed to require people to allow us to park?

16. C   *Sample:* Solution #1—pro: Maybe someone is interested in renting parking space; con: We would need to raise money. Solution #2—pro: We could take civic action; con: We might alienate the neighbors.

17. E   *Sample:* We should pay the businesses that have more space and rent parking spaces from them. It's an easy, efficient solution.

18. E   c. is the only answer that deals with time management.

19. E   *Sample:* studying French—30 minutes

20. A   *Sample:* I could use another 15 minutes of study time to become a better French student.

21. A   *Sample:* 1. studying; 2. household chores; 3. sports; 4. watching TV; 5. hanging out with friends

22. A   *Sample:* If I cut $5 from each of my expenses, I will have another $20 in monthly savings.

23. A   b. is the only answer that reflects the use of math in the real world.

24. E   *Sample:* They balance checkbooks and watch for sales at stores.

25. A   *Sample:* In advertising, formatting draws attention to the product.